S250 Science in Context
Science: Level 2

The Open University

TOPIC 2
Near-Earth objects and the impact hazard

Prepared for the Course Team
by Andrew J. Ball, Simon P. Kelley and Benny Peiser

This publication forms part of the Open University course S250 *Science in Context*. Details of this and other Open University courses can be obtained from the Student Registration and Enquiry Service, The Open University, PO Box 197, Milton Keynes, MK7 6BJ, United Kingdom: tel. +44 (0)870 333 4340, email general-enquiries@open.ac.uk

Alternatively, you may visit the Open University website at http://www.open.ac.uk where you can learn more about the wide range of courses and packs offered at all levels by The Open University.

To purchase a selection of Open University course materials visit http://www.ouw.co.uk, or contact Open University Worldwide, Michael Young Building, Walton Hall, Milton Keynes MK7 6AA, United Kingdom for a brochure. tel. +44 (0)1908 858785; fax +44 (0)1908 858787; email ouwenq@open.ac.uk

The Open University
Walton Hall, Milton Keynes
MK7 6AA

First published 2006. Second edition 2007.

Edited and designed by The Open University.

Typeset by The Open University.

Printed and bound in the United Kingdom by Halstan Printing Group, Amersham.

ISBN 978 0 7492 1887 4

2.1

The S250 Course Team

Andrew J. Ball (*Author, Topic 2*)

John Baxter (*Author, Topic 6*)

Steve Best (*Media Developer*)

Kate Bradshaw (*Multimedia Producer*)

Audrey Brown (*Associate Lecturer and Critical Reader*)

Mike Bullivant (*Course Manager*)

James Davies (*Media Project Manager*)

Steve Drury (*Author, Topic 3*)

Lydia Eaton (*Media Assistant*)

Chris Edwards (*Course Manager*)

Mike Gillman (*Author, Topic 4*)

Debbie Gingell (*Course Assistant*)

Sara Hack (*Media Developer*)

Sarah Hofton (*Media Developer*)

Martin Keeling (*Media Assistant*)

Richard Holliman (*Course Themes and Author, Topic 1*)

Jason Jarratt (*Media Developer*)

Simon P. Kelley (*Author, Topic 2*)

Nigel Mason (*Topic 7*)

Margaret McManus (*Media Assistant*)

Elaine McPherson (*Course Manager*)

Pat Murphy (*Course Team Chair and Author, Topic 1*)

Judith Pickering (*Media Project Manager*)

William Rawes (*Media Developer*)

Shelagh Ross (*Author, Topic 7*)

Sam Smidt (*Author, Topic 7*)

Valda Stevens (*Learning Outcomes and Assessment*)

Margaret Swithenby (*Media Developer*)

Jeff Thomas (*Author, Topics 6 and 7*)

Pamela Wardell (*Media Developer*)

Kiki Warr (*Author, Topic 5*)

The Course Team would like to thank the following for their particular contributions: Benny Peiser (*Liverpool John Moores University; Author, Topic 2*), David Bard (*Associate Lecturer; Author, Topic 6*) and Barbara Brockbank (*Associate Lecturer; Author, Topic 6 and Critical Reader*).

Dr Jon Turney (*University College London and Imperial College London*) was External Assessor for the course. The External Assessors for individual topics were: Professor John Mann (*Queen's University, Belfast*); Professor John McArthur (*University College London*); Dr Richard Reece (*University of Manchester*); Dr Rosalind M. Ridley (*University of Cambridge*); Dr Duncan Steel (*Macquarie University, Australia*); Dr David Viner (*University of East Anglia*) and Professor Mark Welland FRS (*University of Cambridge*).

Contents

Chapter 1

Introduction

This topic is about the **asteroids** and **comets** whose orbits pass close to the orbit of the Earth, and the potential hazard they pose to life on Earth. Collectively, we call these objects **near-Earth objects (NEOs)**. The threat they pose is that an NEO may hit the Earth at high speed, causing events that range from a crater that is only a few tens of metres in diameter and local damage, to eradication of cities, or even to global mass extinction. Scientists have known for centuries that these objects exist and have identified them as a potential future threat, but the likelihood of an NEO impact in our lifetime is considered sufficiently low that more immediate issues such as disease, war and famine dominate people's fears. Rare natural events, such as **tsunami**, **NEO impacts**, **super-volcano eruptions** and earthquakes, are receiving renewed attention as their potential to affect our highly integrated and technology-supported society is better understood. The science of NEO collisions crosses the boundaries between astronomy and Earth sciences, and concerns the detection, tracking and potential effects of NEOs, and the results of ancient impacts on Earth.

Earth scientists study the **Earth system** and its evolution in great detail, and have come to understand that the Earth cannot be viewed in isolation from the surrounding Solar System. Astronomers have studied the sky for millennia, but bodies and events not visible to the naked eye have always seemed unconnected to issues that dominate people's everyday lives. Indeed, we use words like 'alien', 'unearthly' or 'ethereal' to describe things we feel are disconnected from us. This may be why the concept of the sky falling in on us has been used to poke fun at characters with illogical fears. Perhaps the best example is the traditional fable of Chicken Little (or Chicken Licken) who thought the sky was falling when an acorn fell on her head. Chicken Little is ridiculed in her quest to tell the king that the sky is falling. In one version of the story she ends up in a fox's stomach, although a gentler version of the story has her rescued by the king's hounds. The king's reaction to the threat in the latter version is to give Chicken Little an umbrella. Perhaps the king's reaction is a good example of a measured response to an unknown threat.

A more recent example of fear of the sky falling is the story of Vitalstatistix, the chief of a tribe of Gauls in the comic strip series 'Asterix', who evokes his God in battle with the cry, 'By Toutatis!'. Vitalstatistix suffers a dilemma we all face: he is uncertain which of the many risks he faces is most important. As a result, Vitalstatistix's main concern is a fear that the sky will fall on his head, but he has no fear of the hordes of Roman invaders camped outside his village. In an intentional irony, asteroid 4179 has been named (4179) Toutatis, and has an orbit that brought it close (about four times the distance between the Earth and Moon) to Earth in 2004. It is possible (though not likely for many thousands of years) that Toutatis may hit the Earth. Toutatis is interesting from another point of view because it is an unusual tumbling body. It is one of the few asteroids that have been imaged using radar, and appears to be two bodies in contact, tumbling over one another as shown in Figure 1.1. Such rubble piles probably break into many pieces as they pass through the atmosphere, causing several impacts.

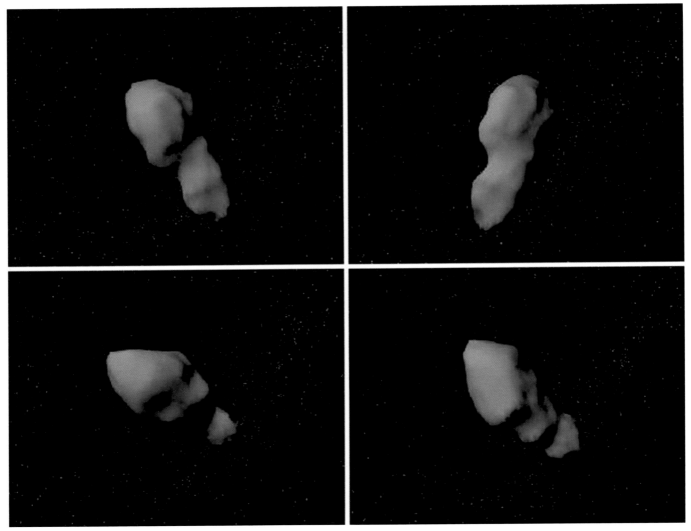

Figure 1.1   Shape of asteroid (4179) Toutatis, calculated from a series of radar observations taken in 1992 and 1996. It is 1.9 km × 2.3 km × 4.6 km in size.

C R E D

As discussed in the *Introduction to the course*, we have adopted margin icons for each of the themes in the early part of the course. In this book we will use the icons for communication, risk and ethical issues throughout, but we will identify the decision-making theme in the first three chapters only. You will be asked to identify this theme for yourself in Activity 4.1 in Chapter 4.

Chapter 1 introduces the Solar System and the threats from rare natural events. Chapter 2 will consider the evidence of past impacts on Earth and their effects. In Chapter 3 you will look at the orbits and population of NEOs, and how they hit the Earth. In the final chapter we discuss the social context of NEOs, and the perception of risk. Definitions of some of the Solar System bodies that are discussed in the text are given in Box 1.1.

Box 1.1 Definitions of some Solar System bodies

Asteroid A small rocky or metallic Solar System body orbiting the Sun. Asteroids are often referred to as minor planets (or planetoids), and many are less than 1 km in diameter. Most asteroids are believed to be remnants of the early Solar System that were not incorporated into the larger planets or were the result of collisions between larger bodies. The highest concentration of asteroids lies within the main **asteroid belt**, between the orbits of Mars and Jupiter.

Comet A small Solar System body similar to an asteroid but composed largely of water ice with other frozen volatiles, dust and various mineral aggregates mixed in. Comets are sometimes characterised as 'dirty snowballs'. Comets orbit the Sun but typically move in highly elliptical orbits that pass far from the Sun into the outer Solar System. The longer the elliptical path of a comet, the longer the time between returns into the inner Solar System (the zone containing the 'rocky' planets, Mercury, Venus, Earth and Mars). Comets with the longest periods originate in a cloud surrounding the planetary system (the **Oort cloud**) extending as far as 3 light-years (a light-year being the distance travelled by light in 1 year) from the Sun, considered to be the limit of the Sun's gravitational influence.

Meteoroid A relatively small (sand grain to boulder-sized) fragment of rock or metal that orbits the Sun. If it enters Earth's atmosphere, the meteoroid heats up, giving rise to a visible meteor (below). Smaller meteoroids are often completely vaporised on entry into the Earth's atmosphere.

Meteor The visible path of a meteoroid entering the Earth's (or another planet's) atmosphere, commonly known as a 'shooting star'. Large meteors are often called fireballs in the media.

Meteorite A meteoroid that reaches the Earth's surface. Meteorites have a range of compositions and have been used by scientists to determine the composition of some asteroids. Some represent the starting material from which planets were derived; other rare meteorites originate from the surface of Mars or the Moon.

1.1 Introducing the Solar System and Kepler's laws

Our planet, the Earth, is in orbit around our star, the Sun. The Sun's gravity constantly attracts the Earth, bending its path through space such that it travels in a closed, nearly circular path around the Sun. The Earth is in such an orbit as a result of the processes that formed the Solar System from a rotating cloud of gas and dust called the **protoplanetary nebula,** about 4600 million years ago. The other planets follow similarly near-circular orbits (Figure 1.2a).

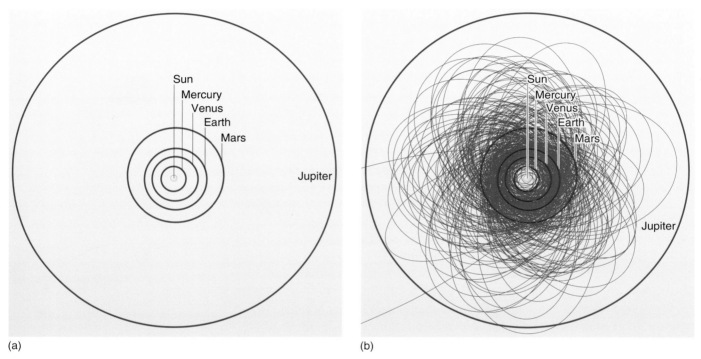

(a)   (b)

Figure 1.2   (a) The most common rendition of the inner Solar System shows the Sun at the centre with Mercury, Venus, Earth, Mars and, a little further out, Jupiter. (b) The inner Solar System with the orbits of some of the known asteroids and comets also shown. It is thought that Jupiter protects the Earth by attracting many asteroids and comets that might otherwise end up hitting the Earth.

Although the traditional image of the Solar System is of orderly, heliocentric (Sun-centred) circles, if you look closely at the orbit of Mercury in Figure 1.2a you will see that, in general, orbits are elliptical. Solar System bodies have orbits that range from near-circular to highly elliptical. A circle is a special case of an ellipse, in which the two focal points (foci) coincide at the centre. In our Solar System, the Sun always lies at one of the foci of the ellipse. This relationship is known as **Kepler's first law**, after the German astronomer Johannes Kepler (1571–1630), who expressed it as 'The orbit of a planet is an ellipse with the Sun at one focus'. Kepler's first law is the basis for understanding the orbits of all bodies orbiting in the Solar System, whether their orbits are near-circular (like that of the Earth) or are highly elliptical, such as comets. The closest and most distant points to the Sun in an orbit are known as the **perihelion** and **aphelion** (plural: perihelia and aphelia, respectively), as illustrated in Figure 1.3.

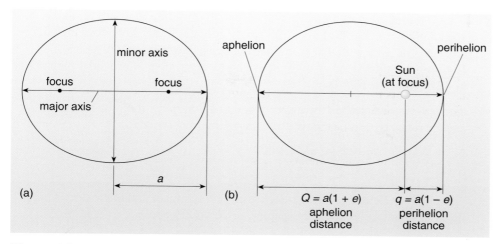

Figure 1.3   Geometry of an elliptical orbit: (a) location of the major and minor axes and foci with the semimajor axis of length a; (b) a Sun-centred (heliocentric) orbit with the Sun at one focus, showing the perihelion and aphelion and two of the equations you will meet in Chapter 3.

The average (mean) of the perihelion and aphelion distances is called the **semimajor axis**, and is given the symbol a. As the name suggests, the semimajor axis is also half of the longer of the ellipse's two axes (Figure 1.3). This is equal to the radius in the case of a circular orbit. For Earth, a is one **astronomical unit** (AU), which is about 1.5×10^8 km or nearly 12 000 times the Earth's diameter. The other planets orbit the Sun with different semimajor axes, ranging from 0.39 AU in the case of Mercury to 39.48 AU in the case of the dwarf planet Pluto. Planets closer to the Sun than Earth, that is, Mercury and Venus, take less than one Earth year to make one orbit, while those further from the Sun take longer. These bodies are not alone; in fact there are many smaller objects orbiting the Sun, ranging in size from particles of dust to objects more than 1000 km across.

Virtually all asteroids orbit the Sun in the same direction as the Earth (**prograde**), though some comets orbit in the opposite, **retrograde** sense. If they collide with the Earth:

- asteroids may be travelling at speeds of 10–30 km s^{-1} relative to the Earth
- comets may be travelling at speeds as high as 75 km s^{-1} relative to the Earth.

NEOs thus contain enormous amounts of **kinetic energy**, which is transformed into other forms of energy including heat, light and sound energy if they impact another body, following the **principle of conservation of energy**. The energy (E_k) released in an impact is given by the equation

$$E_k = \frac{1}{2}mv^2 \tag{1.1}$$

where m is the mass (kg) of the NEO, v is the speed relative to the body being hit (m s^{-1}) and E_k is the kinetic energy (J). You will see later in this book that a great deal of effort has gone into searches for asteroids of 1 km diameter and greater, which could deliver a huge amount of kinetic energy in an impact.

■ If an asteroid 1 km in diameter with a mass of around 1.6×10^{12} kg and a speed relative to Earth of about 20 km s^{-1} hits the Earth, how does the energy released compare with that from thermonuclear explosions? (A typical **H-bomb** would release an amount of energy equivalent to around 1 megatonne of TNT, or 4.2×10^{15} J)

■ The speed needs to be converted from km s^{-1} to m s^{-1} then the amount of energy released can be calculated using Equation 1.1.

$$E_k = 0.5 \times 1.6 \times 10^{12} \text{ kg} \times (20\ 000 \text{ m s}^{-1})^2$$
$$= 3.2 \times 10^{20} \text{ J}$$

3.2×10^{20} J of energy would be released in the impact and explosion. This is the equivalent of 76 000 megatonnes, or 76 000 H-bombs.

This number is difficult to comprehend in comparison with everyday events. To place it in some sort of context, the largest thermonuclear device ever exploded produced 50 megatonnes. The Mount St Helens volcanic eruption in 1980 produced 350 megatonnes, and the Indian Ocean earthquake of 2004, which caused an oceanwide tsunami, released the equivalent of 475 megatonnes of energy. The largest natural explosion in recent human history was the eruption of Krakatoa in 1883, which produced around 5250 megatonnes.

In other words, impacts from the smaller asteroids about which you will learn in this book are more dangerous than the world's nuclear arsenal if it exploded simultaneously, and any volcanic eruption or earthquake in recent history.

1.2 Assessing the risk of rare natural events

R

The impact of a 10 km diameter NEO on Earth would cause catastrophic loss of life and environmental catastrophe on a global scale but, as you will see in Chapter 2, this kind of event has an extremely small likelihood of happening in our lifetime. Smaller NEO impacts of bodies 1 km across happen more commonly, perhaps every few hundred thousand years, but can still have devastating regional effects. Like many low-probability natural risks, the variation in magnitude makes assessing the risk very difficult. In the case of NEO impacts this is compounded by the fact that we have no context into which they fit. Our only close experience might be something like a tsunami. How does society assess such a threat against all the other possible threats to individuals or humankind as a whole?

Most people assess risk in an unconscious way every time they cross the street, as we saw in the *Introduction to the course*. Although everyone has their individual thresholds for risk, we generally accept that the risk of driving to work is small enough to make it worth our while. However, when things are outside our everyday experience, particularly rare events, we are far less able to assess the risk. We could behave like Chicken Little and panic at every conceivable risk to life, but then we would never do anything and that is not a reasonable reaction. In fact, insurance companies make these risk calculations in order to offer life assurance policies, which pay out in the event of accident, injury or early death.

People known as **actuaries** use statistics of the numbers of deaths in large populations, combined with reasoned guesswork, to predict the likely risks involved in a range of activities. That is why a personal insurance premium tends to be higher for those who declare they have a hobby that is a dangerous sport, such as hang gliding.

Actuarial tables of the risk of death from a variety of different threats are generally expressed as simple **probabilities**. For example, if 2.5 million people die every year in the USA and 100 000 of those die in accidents, the probability of accidental death is 1 in 25. For events that do not occur every year, such as flooding or an NEO impact, the risk is averaged over longer time periods but still expressed as a 'per year' figure. Table 1.1 shows an actuarial table for deaths in the USA, including the risk of death from NEO impact. Perhaps surprisingly, the American public appear to be more likely to die in an NEO impact than a flood, tornado or by snake bite. Taken at face value the table implies that people should be more worried about NEOs than floods, but most governments spend far more on flood protection than NEO research.

Table 1.1 Causes of unnatural death in the USA (Chapman and Morrison, 1994).

Cause of death	Probability
motor-vehicle accident	1 in 100
murder or manslaughter	1 in 300
fire	1 in 800
shooting accident	1 in 2500
electrocution	1 in 5000
aircraft accident	1 in 20 000
NEO impact	1 in 25 000
flood	1 in 30 000
tornado	1 in 60 000
bite or sting	1 in 100 000
firework accident	1 in 1 000 000
food poisoning	1 in 3 000 000

Looking a little deeper, Table 1.1 places risks of unnatural death in order, but it is still a flawed technique for comparing such disparate events as death in house fires alongside deaths in rare incidents such as firework accidents, food poisoning, and death in an NEO impact. Table 1.1 includes low-frequency events with high numbers of fatalities (such as NEO impacts) and common events each of which may result in few fatalities (such as fatal car accidents). Consider instead a graph of the probability for the same threats and the estimated fatalities in an individual event. Figure 1.4 shows that many of the threats, such as a shooting accident, firework accident or food poisoning, may kill only one individual, so many such events must occur every year if they are to appear in an actuarial table. Two different NEO impact scenarios are compared on the same graph in Figure 1.4: an event that might happen every thousand years, and an event that might occur only once every hundred million years.

Figure 1.4 Probability of unnatural death resulting from various hazards and number of deaths per incident, based on statistics for the USA, including two different NEO incidents. Note that both axes are logarithmic scales – as the numbers increase, instead of each division being one more than the previous one, each division is ten times the previous.

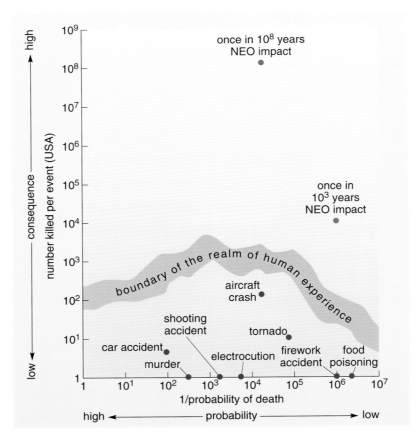

■ Which of the two NEO scenarios appears to dominate in the probability of unnatural death by NEO impact in Table 1.1?

▨ The estimate for deaths resulting from NEO impact in Table 1.1 is dominated by the extremely rare events occurring on average once every hundred million years causing tens of millions of deaths.

C

Although NEO impacts are extremely rare, such events can have truly global effects, as you will see later. However, Figure 1.4 shows that the risk of an NEO impact cannot be reduced to a single figure, and the response of society to this risk has to take account of both the range of likely effects and their probability.

1.3 Society's response to rare natural events

R D

How does humankind respond to other rare natural phenomena that pose a threat to civilisation? One natural hazard that can have devastating effects across nations is giant waves, known as tsunami, which can result from earthquakes under the oceans. Like NEOs, tsunami are rare, natural phenomena that can threaten life on a large scale, though they are more common in some areas of the world, such as Japan (the word tsunami is Japanese for 'wave in the harbour'), than others. In fact, until December 2004, Japan was the centre of some of the worst tsunami disasters in human history (Figure 1.5). The Japan Meteorological Agency can issue a tsunami warning within 3 minutes of an event occurring using data collected from a system of seismographs located around its coast. However, it has long been recognised that tsunami travel long distances across the Pacific Ocean, so that earthquakes close to Japan can affect Hawaii, and movements on the San Andreas Fault along the Californian coast can affect Japan. The relatively wealthy countries surrounding the Pacific Ocean recognised that by collaborating they could reduce the threat posed by Pacific tsunami. The **International Tsunami Information Centre (ITIC)** was established in Hawaii in 1965 by the **International Oceanographic Commission (IOC)** of the **United Nations Educational, Scientific and Cultural Organisation (UNESCO)**. The centre receives data from seismic stations, tidal gauges and buoys across the Pacific. Although tsunami travel at speeds of up to 800 km h^{-1}, they take up to 20 hours to cross the Pacific. The Hawaii centre can analyse earthquake information from many sources and give warnings in less than 1 hour. Thus the arrival times of large tsunami can be calculated and the local media can transmit warnings.

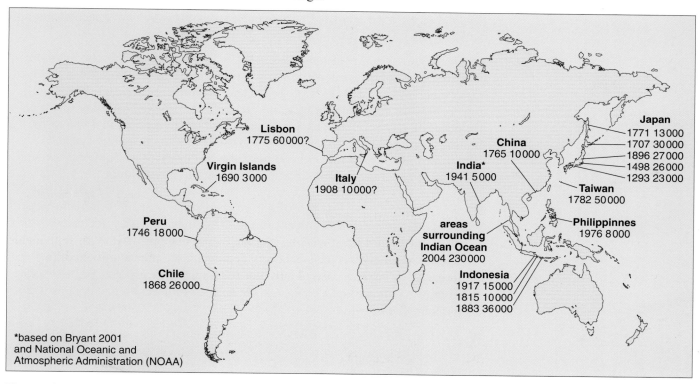

Figure 1.5   Map of the world showing tsunami disasters in recorded human history. The year and estimate of the number of deaths are shown.

On 26 December 2004, one of the largest earthquakes recorded in recent years occurred along a fault zone off the west coast of Sumatra in the Indian Ocean. Unlike the Pacific Ocean, the Indian Ocean had no tsunami warning centre. The lower frequency of tsunami in the Indian Ocean and less-wealthy nations along its rim meant that no equivalent to the ITIC had been established. Note, however, that a tsunami wave can travel across the Indian Ocean to East Africa in less than 9 hours, since that ocean is smaller than the Pacific, and many of the areas worst affected were inundated within an hour of the December 2004 earthquake. On that day, the procedures at the ITIC worked within the constraints under which it operates and, having detected the earthquake, a bulletin was issued within 15 minutes of the earthquake stating that there was no threat to countries around the Pacific. At the same moment, thousands of kilometres away in the Indian Ocean, the tsunami hit land for the first time on the northern coast of Sumatra and the Nicobar Islands.

The ITIC has been able to warn Pacific Rim countries of impending tsunami for many years and is deemed a successful international response to the risk. However, the events of December 2004 show that even this response did not foresee the eventuality that it might predict large tsunami outside the area it was designed to protect. The ITIC came in for criticism in some media reports for not managing to warn people in Indonesia, Sri Lanka and Thailand within the time available. Although an Indian Ocean tsunami warning centre had been proposed prior to 2004, it was not seen as sufficiently high priority and was not funded. The IOC, UNESCO, and governments of countries surrounding the Indian Ocean are now working to establish a tsunami warning centre, but none are yet planned for the Atlantic Ocean or Mediterranean Sea, both of which have seen tsunami in the historical past.

C R

In comparison, NEOs pose a threat less likely to occur in our lifetime but more likely to cause catastrophe, particularly if one hits the ocean. So what is the appropriate response to NEOs? Overreacting and raising public anxiety about low-probability threats might be characterised as a 'Chicken Little' or 'cry wolf' response and has been criticised as scientists whipping up fear in a search for funding for something which would otherwise be low on the public agenda. Conversely, playing down the threat may also be criticised as a cover-up or lead to a false sense of security and too little response to a real threat.

D

■ When a threat has a low probability of occurring on a short timescale, such as a potentially disastrous event like an NEO impact, policy makers respond very slowly for fear of wasting funding on projects for which they will later be held to account. A physical event demonstrating the magnitude of the threat often marks a change in attitude among policy makers. Suggest some examples that marked a change in the attitude of decision makers to a low-probability risk.

▨ You can probably think of several examples, such as the tragically high loss of life in the Indian Ocean tsunami of 2004, the effects of hurricane Katrina on New Orleans in 2005, or the emergence of vCJD, the human form of BSE that you met in Topic 1.

For NEOs and the impact hazard, there has not been a recent impact on Earth to stir decision makers into action, but one has occurred that was visible through a telescope. This was the impact of over 20 fragments of a comet named **Shoemaker–Levy 9 (SL-9)** into Jupiter in July 1994. The story of the discovery of SL-9 dates back to 1992 when it was discovered by Gene Shoemaker, Carolyn Shoemaker and David Levy. They determined that the comet had been broken up into about 23 discernable pieces and predicted that it would actually hit the planet 2 years later in 1994. Because the impact had been predicted, many observations of the comet fragment impacts were made by telescopes around the world. The cameras on the Hubble Space Telescope were able to produce high-resolution images of impact scars. For the first time, a large impact was witnessed in the Solar System, bringing the risk of cosmic impact to the attention of many on Earth who had previously not considered impacts as a threat. The individual pieces of SL-9, now thought to have been piles of loosely aggregated rubble, generated temperatures as hot as the surface of the Sun when they hit Jupiter. Figure 1.6 shows the dark patches that were the aftermath of the impacts as debris rained back onto Jupiter's atmosphere from the impact sites. Each dark patch represents impact debris from deep within the atmosphere, and they are made up of, among other things, hydrogen sulfide and ammonia. The scars remained visible on the surface for several months. The largest ones were larger than the diameter of the Earth, demonstrating the immense amounts of energy dissipated during the impacts.

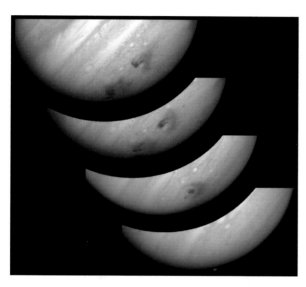

Figure 1.6   Images of Jupiter taken over 5 days by the Hubble Space Telescope during the impacts of the fragments of comet Shoemaker–Levy 9. Note the brown patches resulting from the impacts that change over the 5 days.

Although scientists had been aware of an NEO impact risk prior to the impact of SL-9, there had been little reaction from funding agencies and governments. Subsequent to the SL-9 impacts and several observations of objects passing close to Earth, governments sought advice from scientists and, in some cases, acted, as you will see in Chapter 4.

Although an appropriate response can be triggered by events that bring a risk into public awareness, concern can also be inflamed by events that overplay the risk. Scare stories that exaggerate risk also affect government policy. In this context, the opening lines of *The War of the Worlds*, written by H.G. Wells in 1898 (see below), did not cause alarm in his readers, cause public concern or affect government policy.

No one would have believed in the last years of the nineteenth century that this world was being watched keenly and closely by intelligences greater than man's and yet as mortal as his own; that as men busied themselves about their various concerns they were scrutinised and studied, perhaps almost as narrowly as a man with a microscope might scrutinise the transient creatures that swarm and multiply in a drop of water. With infinite complacency men went to and fro over this globe about their little affairs, serene in their assurance of their empire over matter. It is possible that the infusoria under the microscope do the same. No one gave a thought to the older worlds of space as sources of human danger, or thought of them only to dismiss the idea of life upon them as impossible or improbable. It is curious to recall some of the mental habits of those departed days. At most terrestrial men fancied there might be other men upon Mars, perhaps inferior to themselves and ready to welcome a missionary enterprise. Yet across the gulf of space, minds that are to our minds as ours are to those of the beasts that perish, intellects vast and cool and unsympathetic, regarded this earth with envious eyes, and slowly and surely drew their plans against us.

(Wells, 1898)

c

However, a 1938 radio programme based on the book demonstrated the consequences of misjudging public reaction to this sort of communication. The story of the panic induced by *The War of the Worlds* radio play illustrates the dilemma of trying to communicate low-probability risks to the public, when the events are outside the realm of human experience.

On the day before Halloween, 30 October 1938, millions of Americans tuned into a popular radio series called the 'Mercury Theatre on the Air' that featured plays directed by, and often starring, Orson Welles. What makes this radio play so memorable was the public panic induced by Orson Welles' treatment of *The War of the Worlds* book. The radio play presented the book as a series of news broadcasts, apparently breaking into a music programme.

As the play unfolded, dance music was interrupted a number of times by fake news bulletins reporting that a 'huge flaming object' had dropped on a farm near Grovers Mill, New Jersey. As the radio audience listened intently to these seemingly real news broadcasts, actors playing news announcers, officials and members of the public described the landing of an invasion force from Mars and battle between United States troops and Martian battleships. The broadcast also contained clear explanations of what was being presented, but if listeners missed the brief explanation at the beginning, the next one was 40 minutes into the programme. As they listened to the simulated news broadcasts, as many as 1 million of the 6 million audience concluded that they were hearing an actual news account of an invasion from Mars. People packed the roads, hid in cellars, loaded guns, even wrapped their heads in wet towels as protection from Martian poison gas, in an attempt to defend themselves against aliens. The million people were oblivious to the fact that they were acting out the role of the panic-stricken public that actually belonged in the radio play.

c

In the following weeks there were calls for government regulations on broadcasting to ensure that a similar incident could not happen again, and the victims were also subjected to ridicule in the media. The American public might seem credulous to us, but people knew much less about Mars in 1938, and this was a time before jet engines had been invented or rockets had travelled into space, and the atomic bomb had yet to be developed. *The War of the Worlds* radio broadcast has become the model of needless panic, a modern day 'Chicken Little' fable, which shows the power of mass media to convince people, at least for a short time, of a different reality. For Welles this reaction was something of a triumph, but it illustrates the difficulty of predicting the effects of mass communication. If this level of panic had been prompted by scientists mistakenly announcing an asteroid approaching the Earth, the subsequent public outrage would destroy public trust and might prove a very serious impediment to the perceived credibility of later announcements. Although there has not been an incident as seriously misleading as *The War of the Worlds* play in NEO impact communications, the difficulty of judging public announcements has characterised several scares in recent years, as you will see in Chapter 4.

Summary of Chapter 1

1   NEO impacts are low-probability natural hazards that have potentially catastrophic consequences.

2   Asteroids and comets are members of the Solar System that are smaller than planets, but are subject to the same laws, and in particular Kepler's first law, which states that all orbits around the Sun are elliptical with the Sun at one of the focal points.

3   The danger to life on Earth that asteroids and comets pose comes from their extremely high speeds relative to the Earth. They release huge amounts of kinetic energy in an explosion, should they collide. Even small asteroids have the potential to release more energy than the largest earthquakes, volcanic eruptions and the world's whole nuclear arsenal.

4   The actuarial method of risk assessment (using probability) helps to place the risk from NEO impact in the context of other risks of unnatural death, but this method places the risk surprisingly high on the list. The reason for this anomaly is that the risk from NEO impact is dominated by events that happen on average only once every 100 million years and would be likely to kill many millions of people. It is very difficult to compare this risk with common risks such as food poisoning and firework accidents, which are likely to involve one individual.

5   Communicating a low-probability risk to the public runs the risk of either overplaying the danger and being accused of 'crying wolf', or underplaying it and being accused of covering it up.

Questions for Chapter 1

Question 1.1

Consider two bodies of the Solar System: one is an asteroid and the other is a comet. The two bodies have the same mass, which means that the comet would be slightly larger since comets are dirty snowballs and thus have a lower density. Using Equation 1.1 and estimates of their speed, assess which of the two bodies would pose the greater threat should they impact Earth.

Question 1.2

Briefly describe the two opposite science credibility problems that can arise from a poorly communicated message or a 'scare' story, concerning a low-probability risk to the public.

Chapter 2

The record of NEO impacts on the Earth and Moon

In this chapter we will explore the evidence for past impacts on the Earth and the Moon. Asteroids and comets have been hitting the Earth since it formed, but scientists have only recently been able to unravel the detailed evidence for the number of impacts that have occurred and the consequences of past impacts on Earth. This new knowledge has inspired a search for more craters on Earth and a search of the skies for NEOs that might threaten us.

2.1 Once upon a time long ago

Fireballs in the sky are a fairly common occurrence and you may even have witnessed shooting stars (meteors) in the night sky yourself. The larger fireballs (Figure 2.1) attract widespread interest and regularly feature in media reports, but very rarely have any consequences on the ground. The reports might include photographic evidence, interviews with eyewitnesses, and even video evidence. All this media attention is probably enough to convince you that these things really happened, even though you may not actually have seen the incident. In ancient times such events were thought to be omens and were regarded with fear, but we now have a more complete understanding of the Solar System. Detailed images of many Solar System bodies, even asteroids and comets, have been taken by spacecraft at close proximity and beamed back to Earth, so we are less fearful of fireballs in the sky. Years of study and scientific experimentation have taught us that although meteors look large as they streak across the night sky, they are generally small fragments of rock and ice. If they reach Earth as meteorites, these small fragments of rock weighing from a few grams to a few kilograms can be collected by humankind; although for much of human history they were regarded as curiosities. The world's meteorite collections (including one of the largest collections, belonging to the Catholic Church, which took custody of many meteorites found in medieval times) have fuelled research over many years, and scientists now have a sophisticated understanding of their origin. Meteorites are in fact relics from the early Solar System and thus hold vital clues to its history and evolution. Scientists even organise expeditions to desert regions of the world and Antarctica to collect new specimens, which are preserved by the lack of weathering in the desert and in the sub-zero conditions on the ice. You will see more of our understanding of the Solar System in Chapter 3.

Studies of the Solar System, including both ground-based astronomy and space missions (which you will meet in Chapter 3), have shown that it is made up not only of planets and their moons, but also of many thousands of smaller objects ranging in size from particles of dust up to asteroids that are more than 1000 km across (Figure 1.2b). In fact, extraterrestrial dust falls in a constant fine rain onto the Earth's surface.

■ Around 40 million kilograms of meteorite dust fall to Earth every year. That sounds like a lot, but, to put it in context, calculate how much falls on each square metre of the Earth's surface every year. The surface area of the Earth is roughly 5.1×10^{14} m^2.

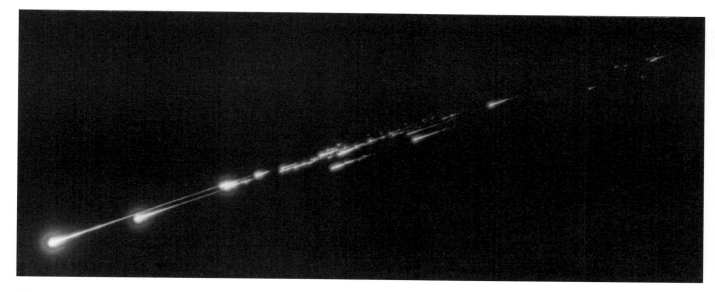

Figure 2.1   A shower of meteors probably originating as a single body that broke up as it entered the Earth's atmosphere.

■ If 40×10^6 kg falls to Earth, then the amount falling on each 1 m^2 of the

Earth's surface per year is $\dfrac{40 \times 10^6 \text{ kg}}{5.1 \times 10^{14} \text{ m}^2}$, which is around 7.8×10^{-8} kg m^{-2}.

■ Meteorite dust varies in size, but, on average, the particles weigh around 1×10^{-5} g. How many pieces of dust fall in each square metre per year? Note the change in units of mass.

■ 7.8×10^{-8} kg is the same as 7.8×10^{-5} g, so dividing the total mass by the mass of an individual grain, 1×10^{-5} g, indicates the mean number of individual bits of extraterrestrial dust falling on each square metre per year, which is seven or eight grains.

Most extraterrestrial material reaches us as dust, not as meteorites, and it has been like this throughout Earth's history. In fact, one of the ways in which scientists measure the deposition rate of ancient oceanic sediments is to measure concentrations of an isotope of helium, which is contained in the constantly falling extraterrestrial dust. ^{3}He is rare at the Earth's surface but much more common in meteorites, since it forms part of the constant stream of charged particles released by the Sun's **corona** called the **solar wind**. The Earth's magnetic field deflects the solar wind, protecting the surface, though some particles interact with the Earth's outer atmosphere, giving rise to the aurora borealis, and ultimately reach the surface. On other bodies, such as our Moon and large asteroids, the dust is an important source of sediment, which is mixed with the debris of impacts, and lies undisturbed for many hundreds of millions of years.

Although you cannot see the finest particles falling, slightly larger particles ranging in size from sand-sized grains to pebbles appear as meteors in the night sky. A regular shower of meteors appear in the sky when the Earth ploughs through the trail of comet Swift–Tuttle and fine particles from the comet enter the Earth's atmosphere. This regular event is known as the Perseid meteor shower, and takes place every year in mid-August. The number of meteorites entering the Earth's atmosphere every year has been a subject for much speculation. The number is now being monitored by remote camera arrays located in several places around the world (e.g. the Nullarbor Plain of southwestern Australia). Occasionally, the observed showers result in meteorite finds. The small rocky or metallic objects have a characteristic melted coating of glassy material known as a fusion crust (Figure 2.2).

1 cm

Figure 2.2 A meteorite showing the shiny coating on one side that resulted from frictional heating as it passed through the Earth's atmosphere.

■ There is reliable evidence that particles ranging in size from dust to small rocks really do fall to Earth and can be collected as meteorites. Can you think of any convincing evidence that very large, perhaps kilometre-sized extraterrestrial objects have hit the Earth in the past?

▪ This is very different to the problem of collecting evidence for the small bodies that fall to Earth because no one has witnessed a large meteorite impact on Earth in historical times. Here, we start to rely on scientific evidence and inference based on reasonable judgement. You might have thought of rare impact craters on Earth, such as the Barringer Crater in Arizona, or perhaps the evidence for a huge meteorite impact at the end of the Cretaceous Period, reputed to have caused the extinction of the dinosaurs. You will learn more about each of these impacts later in this book.

There has been one historical event that most scientists now believe was caused by an extraterrestrial body hitting the Earth. The event was an enormous airburst explosion (an explosion in the atmosphere) around 8 km above the ground over Tunguska in Siberia that occurred on 30 June 1908. The form of the event and its cause have been debated ever since. There is very strong evidence for a huge explosion that flattened and burned the forest for distances of up to 60 km from the centre of the explosion (Figure 2.3). Tunguska is extremely remote and there were no roads or rail link in 1908, so Russian scientists did not manage to mount an expedition to the area until 1927. When they arrived, the scientists found no hole in the ground, not even a shallow scar, and no clear evidence of any extraterrestrial cause, just an area of 2150 km^2 in which trees had been blown down, facing away from a central point (Figure 2.3) and burned (Figure 2.4). This lack of clear evidence for the cause of the explosion has led to a long-standing controversy and speculation with many theories put forward for the Tunguska event, including a comet impact, an antimatter explosion and even the idea that it was the site of an alien spaceship crash. The area was rigorously surveyed 83 years after the event in 1991. Sufficient evidence has been assembled to test the different hypotheses for the Tunguska event. In particular, scientists have recently detected anomalously high concentrations of some rare metals in tree bark and peat layers in the area. This is important because these metals are rare on the Earth's surface but are found at much higher concentrations in some types of meteorite and comet. The consensus is that the Tunguska event was caused by a comet.

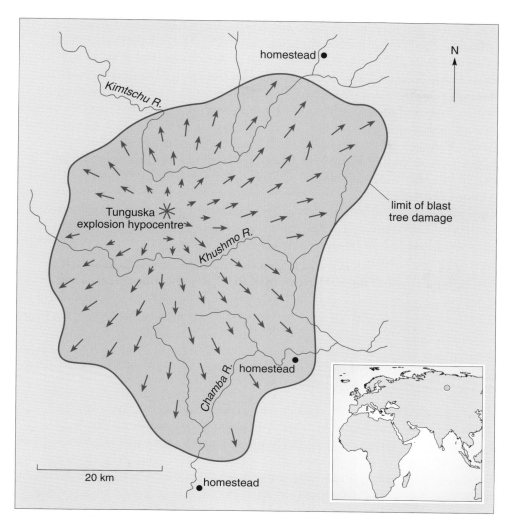

Figure 2.3   Map of the area devastated by the Tunguska explosion of 1908. The arrows indicate the direction in which trees were blown down.

(a)   (b)

Figure 2.4   Photographs of trees damaged in the Tunguska explosion. Image (a) was taken in 1927 and shows the trees stripped, burned and mostly knocked down. Image (b) shows a similar area in 1991. Note that although the forest has regrown, the 80-year-old fallen tree trunks remain visible.

The controversy over the Tunguska event highlights a fundamental difference between science where experiments are designed to test a hypothesis and can generate reproducible results, and science that uses observation or historical evidence and cannot easily be reproduced in a laboratory. The debate about the Tunguska impact lasted such a long time partly because of a lack of evidence. Earth sciences in particular deals with unique events that occurred many thousands or even millions of years ago and, in order to investigate such phenomena, scientists have to use geological evidence to discriminate between different possible hypotheses. A specific example might be observing that one layer of sediment overlies another and deducing that the overlying layer is probably younger. Use of geological evidence to discriminate between hypotheses involves repeatedly testing each hypotheses against the evidence and looking for new evidence (perhaps by visiting different field areas) until peers are convinced of the validity or failure of the hypotheses. In NEO research, there simply is not the option of waiting for the next big impact to happen on Earth in order to proclaim 'we told you so', because the next impact may be thousands of years in the future.

If NEO impact events are not witnessed directly, then why is the evidence so convincing that scientists can be certain such events have occurred and are likely to happen again? The question of what constitutes convincing evidence for a large impact is well illustrated by the search for the cause for one of USA's most famous landmarks, a hole in Arizona known as the Barringer Crater (also called Meteor Crater, or Arizona Crater).

The Colorado Plateau in the state of Arizona in western USA has low relief, although it lies at an elevation of around 1680 m above sea-level. The main feature of the landscape is Canyon Diablo, a sinuous valley that is between 18 m and 26 m deep and drains to the Little Colorado river (Figure 2.5). However, the flat-lying landscape and meandering rivers are scarred by a deep, circular hole in the ground that is 300 m deep and about 1.2 km across (Figure 2.6). In 1906 a mining engineer, Daniel Barringer, and a physicist, Benjamin Tilghman, put forward a hypothesis that the crater was formed by a giant meteorite hitting the Earth. Their hypothesis was not well received or widely accepted, probably because the crater was already well known. Respected geologists of the day had put forward alternative hypotheses that it was the result of either a volcanic eruption or a giant steam explosion. To put the discussion in context, this was a time when a great scientific debate raged over the craters on the Moon; most astronomers believed that all the circular structures on the Moon were volcanic in origin, we now know they are all impact craters.

C   Although Barringer was not the first person to suggest that the crater had been caused by a meteorite impact, he used several scientific arguments that slowly convinced his colleagues in meetings at the Academy of Natural Sciences in Philadelphia, in a series of public meetings, articles in journals and field trips to the crater over a period of several years that this was the case. The evidence he marshalled included:

1   The presence of millions of tonnes of finely pulverised quartz that he believed could only have been created by enormous pressure.

2   The large quantities of melted and part-melted iron, scattered around the rim and surrounding plain.

3   The mixture of melted iron and ejected rocks derived from the host rocks of the Colorado Plateau.

4   The fact that the different types of rock in the rim and on the surrounding plain appeared to have been deposited in reverse order to the underlying rock beds.

5   The absence of any naturally occurring volcanic rock in the vicinity of the crater.

■   The last of Barringer's arguments was that the structure could not be volcanic since there was no evidence of volcanic activity in the crater – no lavas or evidence of a volcano cone. Was he right to use this argument?

▨   As an argument this is a dangerous strategy and shows that Barringer's method of working was not entirely 'scientific'. It sounds as if he had decided that the crater resulted from a meteorite impact and marshalled any facts he could as verification. However, there is a flaw in this line of logic. As the English poet William Cowper said, 'Absence of proof is not proof of absence'. In other words, the lack of lava flows does not disprove the volcano theory; such flows might have been eroded by glaciers, missed or indeed buried by later sediments.

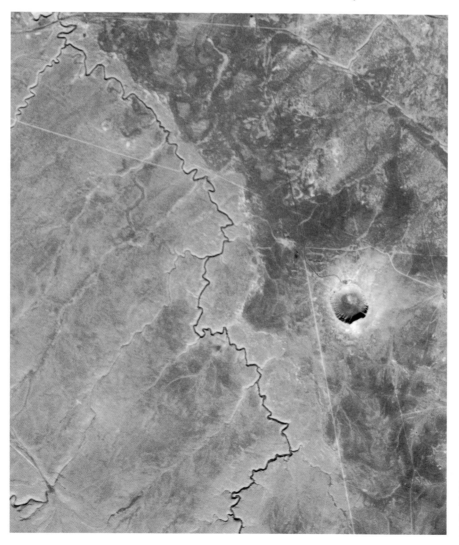

Figure 2.5   Aerial view of the Colorado Plateau showing the Little Colorado river, and the Barringer Crater. The crater is 1.2 km in diameter.

Figure 2.6 An aerial photograph of the Barringer Crater. Note the piles of debris surrounding the hole. This is the same crater as in Figure 2.5.

Our best estimate for the formation date of the Barringer Crater comes from measurements of ^{36}Cl (an unstable isotope of chlorine). ^{36}Cl is formed by **cosmic ray bombardment** of a meteorite while it is in space, but concentrations slowly decrease when the fragments are protected from cosmic rays by the Earth's magnetic field, so it can be used to date meteorite fragments. An age of 50 000 years derived from the meteorite fragments recovered from the area surrounding the crater agrees with ages derived from sediments in the surrounding area. So we can be confident that around 50 000 years ago an iron-rich meteorite crashed through the Earth's atmosphere and hit the Colorado Plateau, probably at speeds of around 17 km s^{-1} (61 000 km h^{-1}) (see Chapter 3). It is likely to have entered the atmosphere at a high angle, although meteorites can enter the atmosphere at angles ranging from vertical to near-horizontal, depending upon their orbit and where it intersects the Earth's surface.

■ Atmospheric pressure falls rapidly to just 10% of that at the surface of the Earth at 17 km altitude and to virtually zero by 40 km above the surface. Given this information, how many seconds might the glow (like a spacecraft re-entering the atmosphere that glows as friction heats its outer shielding) from the meteorite that formed the Barringer Crater have been visible from the ground?

▪ If the body fell vertically, it might have started to glow 2.3 seconds before impact (calculated as 40 km/17 km s^{-1}). If it entered the atmosphere at a lower angle, it might have taken as long as perhaps 5 seconds. In other words, the meteorite would have hit with very little warning.

Like the Tunguska event of 1908, the explosion in Arizona would have devastated the surrounding area. As you will see in Chapter 3, many asteroids are actually loose aggregates of smaller bodies and it seems likely that the impacting body would have broken up during its descent through the atmosphere. The hole in the ground may have been caused by the virtually simultaneous impact of several pieces of meteorite in an area around 400 m across.

■ Scientists have calculated that the Barringer Crater impact body was an iron-rich asteroid around 100 m in diameter, with a mass of 2.6×10^9 kg. Calculate the kinetic energy released upon impact, assuming the body had been travelling at 17 km s^{-1}. Express your answer in megatonnes of TNT.

■ The total kinetic energy in the body can be calculated using Equation 1.1:

$$E_k = \frac{1}{2}mv^2$$

$$E_k = \frac{1}{2} \times 2.6 \times 10^9 \text{ kg} \times (17\,000 \text{ m s}^{-1})^2$$

$$E_k = 3.8 \times 10^{17} \text{ J}$$

Since 4.2×10^{15} J is equal to 1 megatonne of TNT, this would have been an explosive force of:

$\dfrac{3.8 \times 10^{17} \text{ J}}{4.2 \times 10^{15} \text{ J}}$ which is about 90 megatonnes.

The effects of such an explosion on the ground would have depended upon whether or not the body broke up and exploded on entry into the atmosphere (like Tunguska). Larger explosions in the atmosphere might have meant lesser effects on the ground. If we assume the impacting meteorite did not break up in the atmosphere, the explosion on the ground would have released the full 90 megatonnes. The explosion that formed the Barringer Crater, a relatively small impact in the history of the Earth, was thus probably larger than anything humankind has managed to create.

David Kring, a geologist at the University of Arizona, used research on 50 000 years-old fossils and sediments found on the plateau to reconstruct the local environment in Arizona at the time of the impact. He then used mathematical models that were based on nuclear explosions to reproduce the likely effects of the impact. At the time of the impact, the Colorado Plateau was experiencing climate conditions not unlike those of today, although it was perhaps slightly colder. There may have been a few glaciers still remaining from the glacial period around 135 000 years ago in the distant San Francisco peaks, but no general covering of ice. There would have been areas of grassland, woodland communities consisting of pinyon pines and juniper, and denser forest. Mammoths, sloths, bison and camels might have been grazing on the vegetation in grassland areas or browsing on bushes in the woodland (Figure 2.7).

Kring estimated the effects upon flora and fauna in several areas at different distances from the impact.

• At a distance of about 1 km from the final crater rim, the flash from the explosion would have filled the sky. The blast wave would have hit 6.7 seconds after impact, causing a pressure increase of around 2.7 bar (atmospheric pressure is 1 bar and an increase of 0.5 bars causes damage to the lungs of humans), and wind speeds in excess of 1300 km h^{-1}, killing any animal unfortunate enough to be standing in its path. In

Figure 2.7 Reproduction of mammoths and bison grazing in grassland like that found on the Colorado Plateau 50 000 years ago.

grassland, it is likely that soil would have been stripped from the surface and over 1 m of ejected rocks and dust would have covered the ground after the explosion. In short, there would have been total devastation.

- At 5 km from the point of impact, the air blast wave would have hit after about 15 seconds, pressures would have increased by 1.2 bar and wind speed would have reached over 700 km h^{-1}. Even at this distance, 90% of all the trees and large animals would have been killed, and those trees left standing would have been stripped of their leaves.

- At 10 km from the impact, the air blast would have taken about 30 seconds to hit, peak pressures would have increased by around 0.3 bar, and wind speeds would have reached 233 km h^{-1}. Most of the trees would have been stripped of their leaves and many would have been blown over. At this distance, the species of tree and season of the year might have been important. If the explosion occurred in spring or summer, broad-leaved deciduous trees would be more likely to be stripped of their leaves and blown over than narrow-leaved pines; if it was winter, the opposite might have been true.

Animals in the area would have suffered directly from both the blast and from flying debris. The animals would have been more sensitive to the blast wave pressure than the trees, since the shock wave would have compressed the hard and soft parts of the body differentially, causing severe internal injuries. The rapidly changing pressure would have led to massive disruption of their internal organs and death within minutes for those not killed instantly by external pressure, or by flying debris. Larger animals might have been able to withstand greater pressures, but a large majority of animals within 10 km of the impact would have died in the days after the impact.

We can never be sure at what distance it would have been possible to survive such an explosion, but there would have been dangers beyond the simple pressure increase resulting from the blast wave. For example, hiding from the impact, something which we might expect animals to attempt if they had a short time to flee, is likely to have resulted in yet greater danger. The blast wave would have interacted with changes in topography causing extreme local variations in peak pressure. For example, a bison in open grassland would have been thrown through the air by the blast. There would have been the added danger of being thrown against something solid, or hit by flying debris, but the pressure change would have been survivable. A similar animal hiding in a rock alcove or cave might have experienced much higher peak overpressures and been killed. Even at distances of 10 km, the speed of flying debris and the possibility of being thrown against solid objects would have been sufficient to kill.

R The Barringer Crater was formed before human civilisation (humans reached the USA more than 13 000 years ago but less than 50 000 years ago); the effects of a similar meteorite hitting a modern city are likely to be devastating at distances of up to 10 km from the impact. Remember, however, that most of the Earth's surface is still sparsely populated and an impact in a remote area is far more likely than one in a city. The region around the Barringer Crater is still sparsely populated, and the more recent Tunguska event did not kill any humans as far as we know, although the blast was larger than explosions created by humans. In a modern city, such as London, the impact of an asteroid like the one that caused the Barringer Crater, about 100 m in diameter, might kill a large proportion of the

2.7 million inhabitants of the inner city. If such a meteorite hit central London, most of the centre would be flattened, with the older brick buildings being worst affected. Windows would be shattered up to 16 km away and cars might be blown over as far away as the M25 motorway, which encircles the capital around 20 km from the centre. However, the devastation would not be homogeneous. Anomalies might include people surviving on Hampstead Heath, which is sheltered behind Parliament Hill (~100 m above sea level), whereas the devastation would extend much further along the Lee Valley in north London (Figure 2.8).

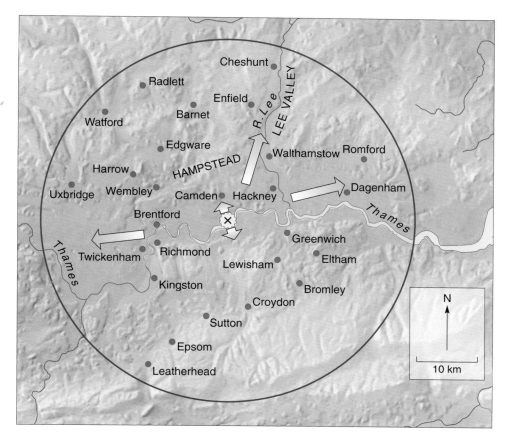

Figure 2.8   An elevation map of London showing the likely shadow area of a blast from a Barringer-sized impact. The topography of London would mean that areas to the east and west along the Thames valley and north along the Lee valley would be worst affected. Areas such as Hampstead Heath and Lewisham might be less affected.

Question 2.1

Given that the area devastated by the Barringer Crater impact was around 25 km across, and the surface area of the Earth is about 5.101×10^8 km², what is the probability of any particular city on Earth being devastated should the Earth be hit (assume a city is around 25 km across)?

The expression for the area of a circle is πr^2, and the expression for the surface area of a sphere (assume for this question that the Earth is spherical) is $4\pi r^2$.

Question 2.2

(a) Which part of the Earth's surface is most likely to be hit by an NEO – land or ocean?

(b) In each case, what would be the main hazard to humankind?

R

Activity 2.1

Allow 2 hours

Go to Topic 2 on the S250 DVD-ROM and start the impact effects activity. Open the activity notes and follow the instructions to model the effects of an NEO impact:

(a) of the size that caused the Barringer Crater in Arizona

(b) if it occurred today in south London.

2.2 The impact record

We have discussed the environmental effects of an NEO impact in western USA, but how many large NEOs have hit the Earth's surface in the past and how many are preserved? Around 170 craters have been confirmed on the Earth's surface, and many more are under investigation. Barringer Crater is only 50 000 years old, relatively well preserved and easily visible as a big hole in the ground. It has overturned sediments on the rim that are surrounded by rock debris and fragments of melted meteorite. But how do scientists recognise craters that are older and partly eroded or filled with sediments? Looking for big holes in the ground might sound very simple, particularly when they can be over 100 km across, but unlike the Moon where even the oldest craters are preserved in exquisite detail (Figure 2.9a), a similar view of the Earth reveals few circular structures (Figure 2.9b).

Figure 2.9 (a) Image of the Moon showing the lunar mare (basalt-flooded areas) marked 'M' and lighter highlands marked 'H'. Both areas are covered in craters. (b) Image of the Earth showing continents and oceans, but no craters.

Mare is the Latin word for 'sea', which early observers thought the darker areas of the Moon resembled.

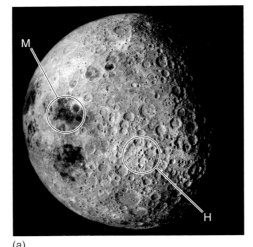

(a) (b)

Impact craters on Earth have the same features as craters on other planets (see Box 2.1). The features vary with crater size. They are particularly difficult to spot because the Earth's surface is constantly being renewed and reworked by the action of **plate tectonics** and erosion. The lack of water and atmosphere on the Moon means there is little or no erosion there and the only reworking of the surface occurs when new impact craters form. Volcanic eruptions last occurred on the surface of the Moon around 3000 million years ago; some areas of the Moon's surface are as old as 4500 million years (the Solar System formed around 4550 million years ago). In contrast, most of the rocks at the Earth's surface are less than 500 million years old. The oceanic crust, which covers three-fifths of the Earth's surface, is constantly being created at **mid-ocean**

ridges and destroyed in **subduction zones**; none is older than 200 million years. The Alpine and Himalayan mountain chains are less than 50 million years old and much of the Northern Hemisphere was resurfaced in the last 3 million years during the most recent Ice Age. The oldest continental crust at the Earth's surface is around 4030 million years old, is only represented by very small fragments of minerals that have been reheated by burial many times since their formation. Thus, in contrast to the Moon, the record of cratering on Earth is constantly removed by erosion, buried by later sediments, or lost down subduction zones. The lack of large crater features on Earth meant that, until quite recent times, Earth scientists did not discuss meteorite impact craters. The standard physical geology textbooks of 30 years ago mentioned the Barringer Crater in Arizona, but no others, and the process of impact cratering did not feature as a geological process on Earth. Indeed, many features we now know to be impacts were once attributed to vague processes such as '**crypto-explosions**'.

Box 2.1 Morphology of impact craters

The size of an impact crater on Earth and other planets depends on the NEO mass and speed, which combine to yield the kinetic energy of the impact. The resulting morphology (size and form) of the crater changes with the size of impact, as illustrated by the different sizes of crater found on Earth. The Barringer Crater in Arizona, USA (Figure 2.6) is an example of a **simple crater**. The crater is a simple bowl shape with a covering of shattered rock and mineral fragments. The crater rims are overturned and ejecta cover the surrounding area. On Earth, these simple craters are generally less than 4 km in diameter.

During larger impacts, the solid rocks are shattered to greater depths beneath the crater floor. Gravity plays an important role as the rocks flow like a liquid during and immediately after the high-velocity impact. The resulting craters take on a more complicated morphology. Slumping of the outer walls causes terracing and rebound of the depressed crater floor creates a central uplift. The 36 million year old Mistastin Crater in Canada is a good example of this form of crater, known as a **complex crater** (Figure 2.10).

Large-diameter craters develop not only a central peak but often one or more peak rings, for example the 290 million-year-old Clearwater Craters in Canada (Figure 2.11). The largest craters on Earth such as the 65 million-year-old Chicxulub (*pronounced chick-sue-lube*) impact crater are **multi-ringed craters** (Figure 2.12)

Figure 2.10 An aerial image of the Mistastin Crater. Note the island in the lake which was formed by the central uplift of the crater. The crater has a diameter of 28 km.

Figure 2.11 An aerial image of Clearwater West and East Craters (Lac à l'Eau Claire) with diameters of 36 km and 26 km respectively.

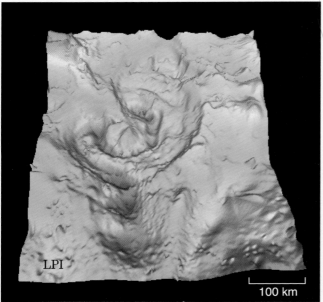

The same progression in crater morphology from simple to multi-ringed craters is observed throughout the Solar System, including on the Moon. One notable difference between lunar and terrestrial impact craters is the larger diameter for each morphological type. On the Moon, for example, simple craters can reach 10 km but they only reach 4 km on Earth. The higher gravity on Earth initiates fluid flow in smaller craters, creating complex craters with central uplift rather than bowl-shaped simple craters.

Figure 2.12 Computer-generated image of the gravity anomaly at the Chicxulub Crater showing multiple rings (the actual crater is buried under hundreds of metres of younger sediment). The total diameter of the Chicxulub Crater is thought to be in the region of 170 km.

Scars of the largest impact craters on the Earth's surface retain sufficient of their original shape and structure to be seen on satellite images, although they are often much diminished. The Manicouagan Crater in Canada (Figure 2.13) is one of the largest preserved craters on Earth. However, even this 100 km diameter crater only became easily visible when a river was dammed to provide water to towns along the St Laurence Seaway. The resulting lake outlines the huge circular structure by filling the depression between the central uplift and crater rim which still remains even though the crater is 214 million years old. There is plenty of other evidence available for those sufficiently intrepid to visit (there are no local roads and the only way in is via the helicopter used by the company that owns the dam).

The Manicouagan structure boasts some of the features we might expect to find in a meteorite impact crater, including circular shape with clear central uplift. Earth scientists have also found other features associated with impacts at Manicouagan, including shatter cones (Figure 2.14a), quartz with planar deformation features (Figure 2.14b), and veins of melted rock produced by friction (known as pseudotachylite, Figure 2.14c) though no tektites (Figure 2.14d) have been found at this site. In addition, the central part of the Manicouagan Crater contains a body of igneous rock that may originally have been a lava lake.

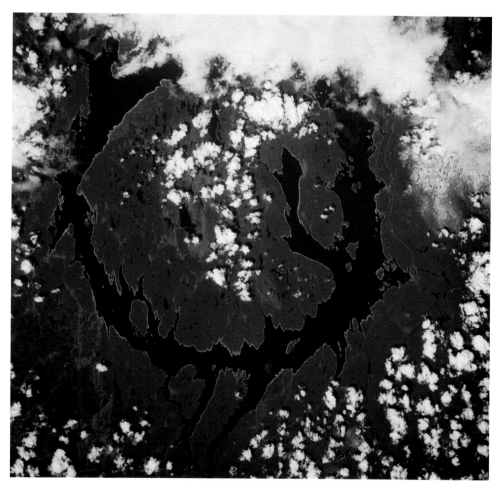

Figure 2.13 Satellite image of Manicouagan Crater, Canada, which is 100 km in diameter.

Figure 2.14 Impact features found in the area surrounding craters on Earth: (a) shatter cones, produced as the shock wave passed through the rock; (b) planar deformation features in a quartz grain seen under a microscope – the image is around 0.1 mm across. These planar deformation features formed as the mineral was instantaneously deformed in the shock wave; (c) pseudotachylite formed as adjacent zones of rock slid past one another during the impact; (d) tektites, which are balls of glass that are formed high in the atmosphere as ejecta condensed (and passed sometimes out of the atmosphere) before falling back to Earth. This example is several centimetres in diameter.

Other impact scars are also filled with lakes which make them clearly visible in aerial photographs. These include the Clearwater East and West Craters in Canada (Figure 2.11) and smaller structures such as the 1.07 million year old Bosumtwi Crater in Ghana (Figure 2.15a). However, not all ancient craters are holes in the ground or circular lakes; many are completely filled and buried, or eroded so deeply that they do not form features in the landscape. Many impact craters have shown up as strange circular shapes in the rock formations discovered when geologists were searching for something else. Some of the oldest craters on Earth appear as faint scars. Even craters as old as 2000 million years, such as Vredefort Crater in South Africa (2023 million years old, Figure 2.15b), and Suavjarvi (around 2400 million years old, Figure 2.15c), still remain. For many years the Vredefort structure was known as a crypto-explosion centre, with many scientists denying its meteorite impact origin. It was not generally accepted to be one of the Earth's largest and most ancient impact structures until the late 1990s.

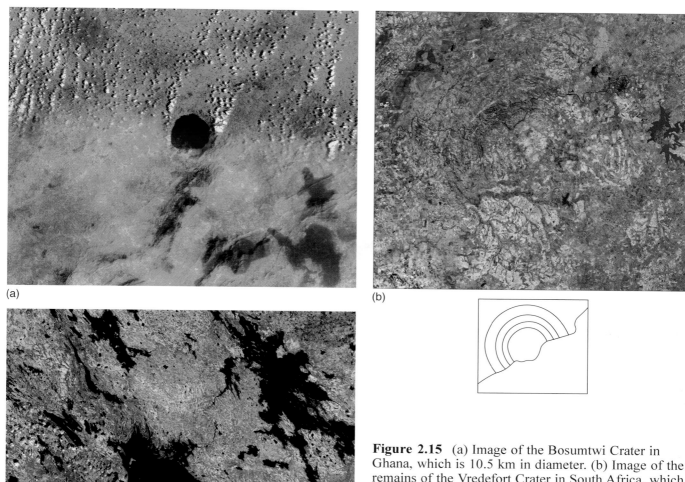

(a)

(b)

(c)

Figure 2.15 (a) Image of the Bosumtwi Crater in Ghana, which is 10.5 km in diameter. (b) Image of the remains of the Vredefort Crater in South Africa, which measures 300 km across. The centre of the crater lies in the middle of the image and multiple circles surround, stretching over halfway to the margin, though they look like ripples in the ground. (c) Image of the Suavjarvi crater in Russia, which measures 16 km in diameter. The crater is so old that it no longer has a circular shape.

2.3 How many holes are there?

R

You have seen that there is strong evidence that the Earth has been hit by large NEOs. This record of impacts also offers the opportunity to estimate the rate of crater formation and perhaps determine the probability that we might experience a large impact in our lifetime. There are currently just 170 confirmed impact craters on the Earth (Figure 2.16). If these craters represented all the impacts that the Earth had experienced over the 4500 million years of its history, the rate would be just one impact about every 26 million years. Note, however, that many impacts leave no lasting trace because they hit oceans and form transient craters in the water itself, giving rise to tsunami.

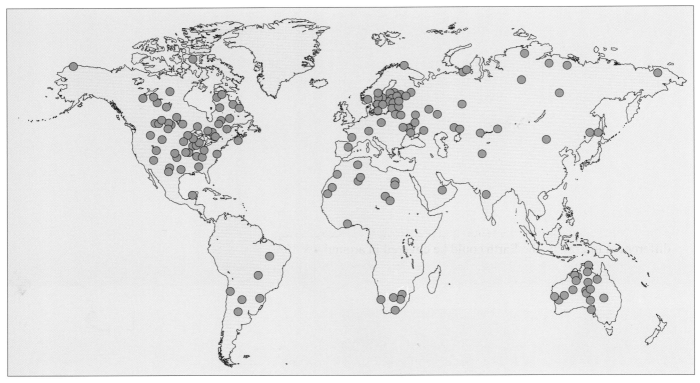

Figure 2.16 Image of Earth showing the localities of the 170 known impact craters.

■ Is the estimate of around one impact every 26 million years a reasonable estimate of the cratering rate on Earth?

▨ No, unlike most other bodies in the Solar System, the Earth has a system of constantly renewed tectonic plates covering its surface. Evidence of ancient impacts is destroyed as colliding plates either form mountain chains or are destroyed by subduction. Ocean crust is constantly formed at mid-ocean ridges and none is older than 200 million years. In addition, the surface is continuously being eroded and shallow features like impact craters are removed, so evidence for many small craters formed on Earth is lost within a few million years.

In order to get an estimate of how many craters might have formed on Earth, we can look at our nearest neighbour, the Moon. The Moon is thought to have been formed from ejecta and impactor materials following a giant impact into the Earth shortly after the latter's formation about 4500 million years ago and it has thus accompanied the Earth throughout most of its history. This means that the Earth and its Moon have experienced a similar rain of asteroids and comets. As you can see (Figure 2.9a), the Moon is covered in craters, large and small, and in many cases, craters formed inside older craters. In fact, large areas of the Moon have reached saturation so that the oldest craters are obscured not by erosion but by more recent craters. Conservative estimates place the number of craters larger than 1 km (the size of the Barringer Crater in Arizona) on the Moon at over 300 000. The Earth presents a larger target to incoming asteroids and in addition its gravity pulls objects more strongly.

■ If the Moon (average radius 1738 km) has around 300 000 craters larger than 1 km in diameter, how many craters should there be on Earth (average radius 6371 km) ignoring any differences in gravitational pull? *Hint*: if they have always been close together, the ratio of the number of craters on the Earth and Moon is approximately the same as the ratio of their surface areas, which can be calculated using the expression $4\pi r^2$.

■ Surface area of the Moon $= 4\pi r^2 = 4 \times 3.142 \times 1738^2$ km^2

$= 3.796 \times 10^7$ km^2

Surface area of the Earth $= 4\pi r^2 = 4 \times 3.142 \times 6371^2$ km^2

$= 5.101 \times 10^8$ km^2

Ratio $= 5.101 \times 10^8$ km^2/3.796×10^7 km$^2 = 13.4$

Thus, without the actions of erosion and plate tectonics and ignoring differences in gravity, the Earth could be covered in around 4×10^6 (i.e. $13.4 \times 300\,000$) craters larger than 1 km in diameter. You might argue that we should ignore the oceans for all but the largest craters since transient craters in water are not preserved. If around 30% of the Earth's surface is land, we should find 1.2×10^6 craters.

Unlike the Earth, the Moon does not have active plate tectonics or an atmosphere that might cause erosion, although long ago it did have active volcanoes. The volcanoes were probably quite like those on Iceland at the present day; they did not have high volcanic cones but probably erupted very liquid basaltic lava flows from fissures, and covered large areas of the surface including earlier impact craters and low-lying areas. The basalt-flooded areas are the dark areas that you can see on the surface of the Moon (Figure 2.9a) on a clear night, and are known as lunar mare. Samples of the lunar mare basalt were brought back to Earth during the Apollo and Luna missions and have been dated in laboratories on Earth.

The total number of asteroids and comets that have hit the Earth is not simply related to the present threat because the rate at which they fall would have been much higher early in Earth's history. Most scientists agree that the Earth was formed by **accretion** as bodies such as asteroids and comets collided and were drawn together by gravity to form a series of larger bodies that are now the planets of the Solar System. The planets continued to attract other bodies and were subjected to a later period of heavy bombardment by asteroids about 4100–3800 million years ago. After that period the rate of bombardment reduced to something like present-day levels. In order to estimate the rate at which craters have formed since the **late heavy bombardment**, scientists have used the number of craters on the lunar mare that formed around 3600 million years ago. (The mare were probably erupted over a period of 100 million years, but we will use 3600 million years as an approximation.)

■ Briefly explain why scientists use the cratering rate on the lunar mare rather than the whole Moon to estimate the rate of crater formation on the present-day Earth.

■ Scientists use the lunar mare because the rate of bombardment is easy to work out since they erupted at around the same time. Some areas of the Moon's surface have less well known ages and may be as old as 4500 million years. The older areas also suffered the late heavy bombardment around 4100–3800 million years ago when the rate of cratering was much higher than it is now. If the whole surface of the Moon were used, the resulting cratering rates would be biased towards this early part of our planet's history, not the present day.

However, in order for this calculation to yield realistic numbers, the rate of cratering must have been the same over the last 3600 million years (since the lunar mare were erupted). If the number of NEOs impacting has decreased through time, the average value from crater counting on the mare would be biased towards times of heightened impacts.

The crater sizes have also been measured using high-resolution photographs taken by spacecraft in orbit around the Moon so that scientists can calculate the formation rate for different sizes of crater. Figure 2.17 shows the results of this work as the number of craters of a particular size plotted against crater diameter. We have used this plot rather than the total number formed in 3600 million years because the average age of the Earth's surface is 100 million years.

■ Using Figure 2.17, estimate how many craters greater than 10 km in diameter form on the Moon in 100 million years.

■ Drawing a line vertically from 10 km on the crater diameter axis until it intersects the diagonal line for lunar craters and then drawing a line horizontally to the 'craters per 100 million years' axis, indicates that around 30 craters larger than 10 km in diameter form on the Moon every 100 million years.

Figure 2.17 Plots showing cratering rates for the Earth and Moon. Each shows the number of craters formed per 100 million years that are *larger* than particular sizes. The lines slope down to the right because large craters are created less frequently than small craters. Note also that the scales on both axes of this graph are logarithmic (see Figure 1.4). The reason for using this type of graph is that it makes the relationship between crater diameter and formation rate easy to examine. The lower solid line represents data derived from 3600 million years of impacts on the lunar mare; the upper solid line uses data derived from impacts over the last 125 million years for craters on Earth. The dotted line represents the values for 13.4 times the lunar data (the ratio of the surface areas of the Earth and the Moon) for comparison with the terrestrial data.

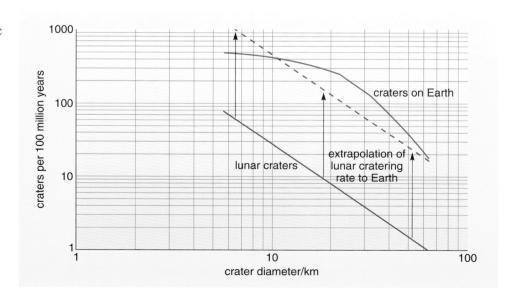

It is not possible to check the number of craters that have formed on Earth in the same way as the Moon because the surface is reworked. However, there have been several attempts to estimate the rate at which large craters form by counting those formed during the last 100–200 million years. Although the Earth is covered in tectonically active areas, including fault zones, mountains, volcanoes, and mid-ocean ridges, there are areas that are tectonically quiet. They are called **cratons** and are generally old pieces of continental crust, including large areas of Australia, North America, and some parts of Europe and Africa. In these areas, the land surface is renewed much less rapidly than in mountainous areas such as the Alps or Himalayas and evidence can still be found for meteorite impacts many millions of years after the event.

Finding the age of craters on Earth is quite difficult, since the evidence may be just a few shattered rocks or unusual layers in the sediments. In other cases, there are no ejecta layers to give precise ages, so Earth scientists have to bracket the age using the age of the rocks hit by the meteorite and the age of sediments filling the crater.

Gene and Carolyn Shoemaker worked on large impact craters in Australia, where such craters can be preserved for many hundreds of millions of years. Using only craters larger than 20 km diameter, the Shoemakers calculated a rate of meteorite collisions with Earth over the last 100 million years of 5×10^{-15} km^{-2} y^{-1}. They derived this number by dividing the area of old continental crust in Australia into the number of craters formed in the last 100 million years.

■ Using the Shoemakers' estimate of the formation rate for craters larger than 20 km, calculate the number of craters that would form on the Earth every 100 million years, given that the surface area of the Earth is around 5×10^8 km^2.

▪ Multiplying the crater formation rate (5×10^{-15} km^{-2} y^{-1}) by the surface area of the Earth (5×10^8 km^2) yields 2.5×10^{-6} collisions per year, or 250 craters larger than 20 km every 100 million years.

David Hughes, a British astronomer, estimated the rate of formation of craters younger than 125 million years for craters over a range of sizes by comparing several of the world's most stable pieces of crust, and obtained similar rates for large craters for each of those areas (Table 2.1).

Table 2.1 Hughes' estimates of crater formation rates on Earth over the last 125 million years.

Crater diameter/km	Crater production rate/km^{-2} y^{-1}	Crater formation rate on the Earth's surface/100 million years
4.00–5.66	7.7×10^{-16}	39
5.67–8.00	9.9×10^{-16}	51
8.01–11.30	14.0×10^{-16}	72
11.31–16.00	17.0×10^{-16}	87
16.01–22.60	23.0×10^{-16}	118
22.61–32.00	15.0×10^{-16}	76
32.01–45.25	7.0×10^{-16}	36
45.26–64.00	3.4×10^{-16}	17

- Do the estimates produced by Hughes and the Shoemakers agree to within reasonable bounds? (Compare craters larger than 16 km in the Hughes study with the value obtained by the Shoemakers.)

- Yes, the number of craters larger than 16 km diameter forming every 100 million years is 247 (118 + 76 + 36 + 17), which is almost the same as the number for Australia estimated by the Shoemakers, even allowing for the difference in diameters used (the Shoemakers used craters larger than 20 km).

We can now test the assertion that the Earth and Moon should have similar cratering rates because they share the same history. If cratering rates have remained similar for over 3600 million years, the rates derived from the lunar mare and Earth's cratons should be approximately the same. Figure 2.17 shows data from the study of Hughes plotted as a cumulative number in the same way as the lunar data. The data clearly show that there have been more impacts on Earth for any given crater size, as you would expect given that Earth is a larger body, and, as we calculated earlier, should have around 13.4 times more impacts. The dashed line on Figure 2.17 represents 13.4 times the values calculated from the lunar data and, as you can see, they overlap the data for Earth's cratons. The numbers do not coincide completely: the terrestrial data yield a curve with slightly higher values than predicted for large craters but less for small craters. These numbers are in reasonable agreement (they are within a factor of two) and there are other factors that we have not taken into account, but might also play a role, such as the effects of the Earth's atmosphere and its greater gravity. However, an alternative interpretation is that the data might indicate a higher crater formation rate in recent times (the last 125 million years) compared with the whole of the last 3600 million years, something that is currently debated in the scientific community.

- Can you suggest a reason why there seem to be fewer small craters on Earth, given that the smaller ones on the Moon seem far more common?

- A reasonable suggestion might be that there are fewer small craters because they are shallower and thus more easily eroded, or buried, or alternatively the small ones are more difficult to find and so not all have yet been discovered.

Hughes also paid attention to the loss of small craters and studied the relationship between crater size and age. He reasoned that if smaller craters are being preferentially eroded, it would mean the average age of the smaller craters should be younger than the average age of larger craters. Although he found that very small craters are likely to be lost by erosion, those larger than 1–2 km diameter showed no relationship between crater age and crater size. More recent work on modelling asteroid impacts has shown that while the largest asteroids penetrate the Earth's atmosphere intact, many smaller bodies break up on entry, sometimes exploding like the Tunguska body, and form no crater. Thus the apparent dip in numbers of smaller craters seen in Table 2.1 may also be a physical effect of break-up during entry into the Earth's atmosphere rather than erosion of small craters.

Finally, Hughes was not able to shed light directly on the formation rate of craters as large as the 65 million year old Chicxulub Crater in Mexico (Chicxulub is over 150 km in diameter) because there are so few craters larger than 64 km. An approximate formation rate for craters over 100 km in diameter can be extrapolated from lunar mare data and is, on average, one every 100 million years.

2.4 The significance of NEOs in Earth history

R

NEO impacts certainly dominated the environment on Earth in its early history through to the late heavy bombardment around 4100 to 3800 million years ago, but since then the crater formation rate has been much more constant and much lower. There is a debate concerning the importance of NEO impacts both to life on Earth and, more recently, their importance during the history of the human race. The largest and rarest events (such as the end-Cretaceous impact at Chicxulub) had catastrophic results on a global scale, but Earth scientists have shown that not all such large impacts leave a lasting record of mass extinction. Smaller NEO impacts that have occurred during the time the human race has been on Earth are not well documented in written historical records, though there is strong evidence that several impacts have occurred in the last few millennia.

The Chicxulub impact that took place around 65 million years ago devastated large areas of the American continent and left a thin layer of dust and debris covering the whole planet. Although there is debate in the scientific community about its importance across the whole world, it is clear that the impact contributed to the extinction of many species of flora and fauna at the end of the Cretaceous (Figure 2.18 overleaf). Despite the extreme rarity of such impacts (such events occur on average only every 100 million years, as you saw in Sections 1.2 and 2.3), this type of event dominates the calculations of risk today because it is capable of affecting the whole planet.

Overall, some 65% of species on Earth disappeared at the end of the Cretaceous, but research in different areas of the world shows that the effects of the meteorite impact were very variable. It seems that areas more distant from the impact site yield evidence for a much less dramatic change at the end of the Cretaceous. In addition, while some scientists maintain that there was more than one impact around the time of the **K/T boundary** (Figure 2.18), many others refute this idea. Evidence from recent drilling within the Chicxulub Crater has produced controversial results. Still others are exploring the importance of the smaller Boltysh impact in Ukraine which also formed at the end of the Cretaceous Period. Finally, several scientists have commented that the eruptions of large volcanic provinces, known as flood basalts, are correlated with periods of extinction in the fossil record. In this context, there seems to be strong evidence that the Deccan flood basalt volcanism in India contributed to climate change in the last few million years of the Cretaceous Period. While there is a scientific debate concerning the combination of mechanisms that led to the mass extinction at the end of the Cretaceous Period, what no one now doubts is that the devastation wrought by the impact of a 10 km asteroid 65 million years ago was an important factor in the events.

K/T boundary: 'K' is the international symbol used for the Cretaceous and 'T' is short for Tertiary, which is the old name for the Palaeogene and Neogene Periods.

Figure 2.18 A stratigraphical column for the Phanerozoic showing the periods and epochs into which Earth scientists have divided time. The K/T boundary 65 million years ago marks one of the most important changes and the boundary between the Mesozoic and Cainozoic eras. Note the scales for time are different for each era.

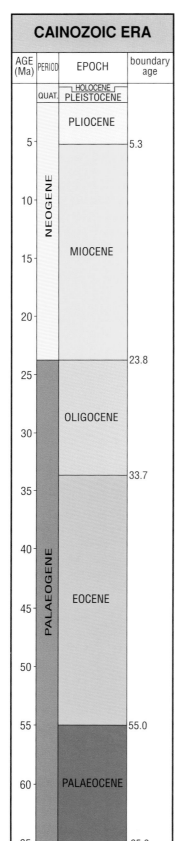

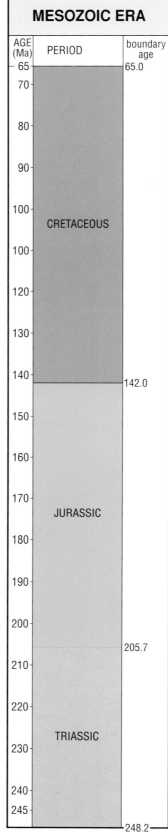

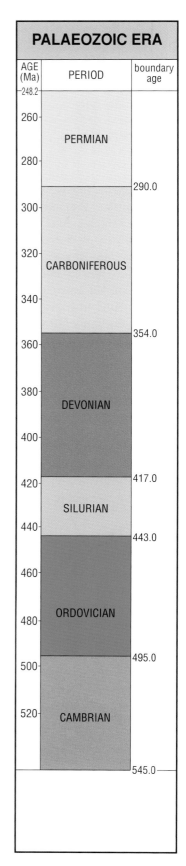

Before leaving with the idea that the Chicxulub impact was a global disaster and catastrophe for all involved, bear in mind that this also marks the point at which mammals rapidly diversify to inherit the world left by dinosaurs. Without the Chicxulub impact, mammals might not have evolved in the way they did, and we might not be here to discuss NEOs and the impact hazard!

Activity 2.2

Allow 30 minutes

Go to Topic 2 on the S250 DVD-ROM and start the NEO impact effects calculator. Open the activity notes and follow the instructions to calculate the effects of the Chicxulub impact in the Gulf of Mexico at various distances from the crater. Comments on the activity can be found on the DVD-ROM.

The record of craters on the Earth's crust implies that there must be a regular rain of impacts, creating craters 20 km in diameter at the rate of around 2.5 every million years (roughly 1 per million years on land); even the largest impacts probably occur at a rate of one every 100 million years. It should thus be possible to identify impact events other than the end-Cretaceous event and assess whether meteorite impacts have commonly been associated with mass extinctions.

Another period of heightened meteorite impacts on Earth has in fact been identified. It occurred around 35.5 million years ago during the Eocene epoch (Figure 2.18) and involved at least two huge craters that formed within a few thousand years of one another:

- the Popigai Crater (35.7 million years old) is about 100 km in diameter and formed in what is now Siberia
- the Chesapeake Bay Crater (35.5 million years old) is about 90 km in diameter and formed in eastern USA.

The age difference between the two craters is so small that it lies within the uncertainty of the dating techniques. However, we know they formed at least several thousand years apart because two layers of microscopic glass balls, known as tektites (Figure 2.14d), have been found in deep-sea sediments that are separated by several centimetres of clay. It may be that other craters of similar age remain to be found, and at least three other craters have been assigned less-certain ages that might mean they are part of a cluster of craters that formed around 35.5 million years ago. The fact that two such large impacts occurred so close together in time is strong evidence of a cluster of related impacts. (Such large craters occur only on average every 10–100 million years, so two within half a million years is extremely unlikely.) There is also evidence of heightened concentrations of extraterrestrial dust in deep-sea sediments for around 1 million years either side of the large impacts. The Eocene cluster is thought to have been caused by a shower of comets, because mathematical models indicate that a disruption in the Oort cloud would cause a comet shower that would last between 1 million and 3 million years. However, despite the apparently large and clustered impacts, the Late Eocene Period was not a time of significant mass extinction or sudden climate change. Clearly not all large impacts have the same devastating effects as the one at the end of the Cretaceous.

In fact, there are several other cases where scientists are still debating the relationship between mass extinctions and possible impact events. As you saw earlier, a very small proportion of terrestrial craters is preserved, and in many ways the crater record is like the fossil record. Like fossils, many impact craters are eroded or buried out of sight, so it is likely that we could find evidence for impact events in sedimentary layers but not the crater that was the source of the event. In fact this was the case for the end-Cretaceous immediately after 1980 when the impact layer had been identified in sediments but no crater had been found. At the time of writing (2005), there are no other impact events and craters so closely tied to a major event in Earth history as the Chicxulub Crater is tied to the K/T boundary mass extinction. There are, however, debates about several events, including the largest ever mass extinction at the end of the Permian Period, 250 million years ago, but the evidence is by no means as strong as for the end-Cretaceous event.

R

The debate over the devastating effects of a 10 km diameter asteroid impacting the Earth is important for scientists trying to understand the evolution of the Earth and the future of humankind. However, we can do very little about such bodies other than maintain a constant programme searching for new asteroids and comets and keeping track of them. The population of NEOs is slowly depleted by collisions but is also constantly replenished from the asteroid belt and the outer Solar System, a situation which has probably been the same for over 3600 million years. Perhaps a more important question for the future development of human civilisation should be the likelihood and effects of a smaller body hitting our increasingly interconnected and interdependent world. 'City killer' asteroids, 50–100 m in diameter, such as the one that caused the Barringer Crater, might cause tsunami or wipe out populous regions. They occur on average every few thousand years.

■ An extrapolation of the lunar mare data in Figure 2.17 indicates around 2200 craters, 1 km in diameter, form on the Moon every 100 million years. Using this number, calculate the rate of formation of 1 km craters on Earth, and comment on factors which would affect the reliability of the resulting number.

▨ Based on this extrapolation, around three craters would form on Earth every 10 000 years or, on average, one every 3300 years ($2200 \times 13.4 = 30\,000$ (to two significant figures) craters per 100 million years). Remember, however, that 70% of these will fall in the oceans and the craters will be lost seconds after the impact. This cratering rate is dependent on assumptions that the cratering rate has not changed over the last 3600 million years. It also assumes that small bodies are not affected by the Earth's gravity and that they do not break up in the atmosphere.

Given these caveats, the formation rate of one crater every 3300 years on average is only an order of magnitude estimate, and 1 km craters probably form on the continents around one every 10 000 years on average. Other estimates have been made, and most conclude that 1 km diameter craters form on Earth 'every few thousand years'.

Thus, by using data from the Moon, scientists can show that events like that which formed the Barringer Crater (50 000 years ago) occur about every ten thousand years and, by a similar extrapolation, events such as the Tunguska explosion (about 100 years ago) occur every 2000–3000 years. Such events might have been recorded by humans as catastrophes to ancient civilisations. The problem is that most histories were not written down at the time the events occurred. Apart from some notable individual accounts, such as the famous eruption of Mount Vesuvius recorded by the younger Pliny in AD 79, major natural events are very difficult to verify to the levels of certainty required by scientific investigation. Events such as the catastrophic explosion of Santorini (reputed to have caused the demise of the Minoan civilisation on Crete) have been verified only from tree rings which show several years of poor growth. There are several well-documented NEO impact craters formed during times when humans lived on Earth that are likely to have at least been indirectly witnessed. The Barringer Crater formed 50 000 years ago, but humans are thought to have reached North America only about 13 000 years ago (although some argue that it may have been as much as 30 000–40 000 years ago) so it is unlikely to have been witnessed directly. In fact, there are no clear descriptions of humans having witnessed an impact other than the Tunguska event in 1908. Although the area was largely uninhabited, a few fur traders and local tribespeople were in the area and witnessed the explosion. In fact, a driver stopped a trans-Siberian railway train as the noise and explosion made him worry the train might derail.

The circumstantial evidence that humans have witnessed large NEO impacts is strong. A 14 km crater in Kazakhstan formed just 900 000 years ago, and a 1.9 km diameter crater formed in Estonia 2400 years ago. Perhaps we should be more disturbed to find that even modern craters are not well documented, such as the Wabar Craters in Saudi Arabia, the largest of which is 116 m in diameter and only around 140 years old.

So why have NEO impact events not been clearly recorded? Perhaps they have just occurred in uninhabited areas, or perhaps they were recorded in myths or in oral histories as explosions or fires. The problem is separating evidence for an NEO impact from other locally devastating events. One example that has been much debated in the media and literature has been the sudden period of cold and crop failures recorded in the 6th century. Oak trees found in Irish peat bogs and timber in old buildings show a consistent reduction in tree growth between AD 536 and AD 545. Similar cooling and slower growth is also recorded in America and Asia. The estimated average reduction in temperature is of the order of 3 °C and some limited Chinese records of the same time talk of a dust veil obscuring the Sun. In addition, the 6th century monk Gildas talks of widespread wildfires and destruction of the landscape. Gildas had been thought to be talking allegorically; he also used many biblical references. However, other writers talk of darkness, reduced sunlight and short days around the same time. This was also a time of extreme hardship in Europe, and a time when the overall population decreased, possibly as a result of the first appearance of the Black Death in the area. Crop failures resulting from climate cooling may have increased susceptibility to this disease among a weakened population.

One question concerning this type of evidence is whether these observations of climate effects, darkness and disease are necessarily linked. In fact they may be linked, but we have to be extremely careful with historical and anecdotal records like these since they are difficult to verify and set precisely in time. The differences between the dates in the various reports may be decades and could well be reporting different phenomena. In addition, many reports were written by later historians who were not present at the event but repeated earlier accounts and which may appear to confirm them. It has been argued that the accounts from China are describing the effects of a huge forest fire or a more local volcano eruption of which the author was not aware. As an example, many people in Europe were mystified by a dry acrid fog which led to increased deaths in eastern England during 1783–84. In fact the fog was caused by the eruption of an Icelandic volcano, Laki.

Two hypotheses have been advocated for the 6th century event. One suggestion has been a major volcanic eruption. However, the best evidence for ancient volcanic eruptions are acid-rich layers in ice cores from Greenland and Antarctica, but they appear to have slightly different ages from the events reported in historical records. Studies measuring acid levels in ice cores record many of the known prehistoric eruptions. Some acid layers in the Greenland ice cores have been assigned ages of AD 528 and AD 533, and an acid layer recorded in Antarctica has an age of AD 504 ± 40 years, but none of these layers has the concentrations expected for a major volcanic eruption.

■ Does this rule out the volcano option for cooling between AD 536 and AD 545?

▓ It probably does rule out a major eruption although care is needed with this interpretation because correlations depend on the precise dating of both the tree rings and the ice-core layers. In addition, if an eruption came from under water, the acid would be preferentially dissolved in the ocean, depressing any signal that might appear in the ice core.

The second hypothesis for the 6th century event is a meteorite or comet impact, which might explain the dust veil observed. Against this hypothesis is the lack of any crater identified for this time, even though the intensity of the event seems to have been greater in northern Europe, which was well populated by literate people who might have been expected to record such an explosion. However, as the Tunguska event showed, there may not be a large crater if the body exploded in an airburst well above the ground, and at distances from the impact it may be difficult to determine the source. If this happened, forest fires ignited by the explosion might explain the apparent dust veil. Mathematical modelling has recently shown that a comet fragment just 300 m across would be sufficient to cause the observed effects. Further, astronomers have identified a source, the Taurid meteor stream, which is thought to be the result of a comet break-up some 20 000 years ago. The Earth passes through the Taurid stream in June and November each year and the comet impact hypothesis holds that there was a fragmentation around AD 500 and that the impact occurred as the Earth passed through the stream in early AD 536 (although this figure is based on a very large extrapolation from the known observations).

There is no corroborative evidence for the comet hypothesis in the ice cores, and no reports of humans hearing an explosion which might be expected for a Tunguska-type event. So how should we consider the AD 536 event? Although there has been more than one book on the subject, and several TV documentaries, there is currently too little scientific evidence to test the hypotheses and we have to await further evidence, possibly in the form of chemical variations in lake sediments of the same age. Although the comet impact hypothesis is reasonable and plausible, it is as yet unsupported by quantitative evidence. The evidence for the AD 536 event cannot really help us to understand the hazard from NEOs since we cannot yet demonstrate the involvement of a comet or asteroid body. The estimates based on crater counting on the lunar mare remain one of the most reliable sources of information on small craters.

Summary of Chapter 2

1   There have been many small NEO impacts on Earth in the last million years, but two events have been studied in detail, the Tunguska event in 1908 and the formation of the Barringer Crater 50 000 years ago, which provide useful models for the likely results of future NEO impacts.

2   Mathematical models based on nuclear explosions can be used to estimate the likely damage that might be caused by an NEO impact. The damage extends far beyond the physical crater.

3   The impact record on Earth consists of around 170 craters, but this is far fewer than the number of NEOs that have collided with Earth.

4   The surface of the Earth is constantly reworked by tectonic processes and erosion. The surface of the Moon, on the other hand, is not subject to such processes and illustrates what the surface of the Earth might have looked like if it had been inactive.

5   Based upon craters in stable areas of the world, on average two to three 20 km diameter craters form somewhere on the Earth every million years, and a 1 km crater forms on average every ten thousand years (such small impacts would not leave lasting craters if they fell in the ocean).

6   Evidence for recent impacts in human history is very difficult to verify, though the human race must have witnessed several NEO impacts.

Questions for Chapter 2

Question 2.3

(a) Compare the impact rates for the surfaces of the Moon and Earth (Figure 2.17). Explain whether or not these estimates are within reasonable bounds.

(b) Briefly describe what implications your answer to (a) has for changing meteorite collision rates over the last 3600 million years.

Question 2.4

There is only one large crater confirmed to be less than 1 million years old, the 14 km diameter Zamanshin Crater in Kazakhstan, which is 0.9 million years old. Does this mean that we are overdue for a large impact on Earth?

Chapter 3

A population of celestial bodies

3.1 Introduction

In this chapter you will look at objects that impact the Earth, causing the range of effects discussed in the previous chapter. Most of these NEOs are asteroids made of rock and metal, although a small fraction of NEOs are comets, which are made of icy material. Most asteroids and comets spend all their time well away from the Earth, further out in the Solar System. As you saw in Chapter 2, however, some pass close to, and even collide with, the Earth. The answers to the following questions covered in this chapter should help you understand the science behind these occasional visitations of high-speed objects falling from space:

- How do the Earth, asteroids and comets move in orbit around the Sun?
- What are asteroids and comets?
- Why do some NEOs come close to the Earth?
- What is the size and diversity of the population of NEOs?
- How are NEOs detected, tracked and characterised?
- What is the nature of the probability, uncertainty and predictability of NEO impacts?

In order to understand the nature of NEOs as a population of celestial bodies, it is necessary to be aware of some of the physics of orbital motion and the way in which the properties of NEOs are quantified. This necessarily involves some mathematics. The essential points to extract from this chapter are the ways in which several parameters depend upon one another, and their implications for our understanding of the NEO hazard.

3.2 The Solar System and more on Kepler's laws

c

As you saw in Chapter 1, the planets follow orbits around the Sun, which lies at one of the two focal points of an elliptical orbit path as described by Kepler's first law. While many Solar System objects such as planets, asteroids and comets are in heliocentric orbits, other objects can also be in orbit around planets and, as we shall see later, even around asteroids. Our own Moon is in orbit around the Earth (as indeed are thousands of artificial satellites). Astronomers use a series of well-established equations to characterise each Solar System body's orbit and thus are able to predict where it might be at any particular point in time. This is in effect the language astronomers use to talk to each other about the Solar System.

An important equation that scientists use to describe the physics of orbital motion relates the semimajor axis a (which you met in Chapter 1) to the orbital period P (the time it takes to make one orbit):

$$P^2 = ka^3 \tag{3.1}$$

where k is a constant (of proportionality) that depends on the mass of the body being orbited. This is known as **Kepler's third law**. (You will meet Kepler's second law in a moment.)

■ Using Equation 3.1, determine whether the orbital periods of planets further from the Sun are longer or shorter than those close to the Sun.

▨ Orbital periods of planets further from the Sun are longer. This is because as a increases in Equation 3.1, P also increases.

For everything that orbits the Sun, the constant k has the same value, so the ratio of P^2 to a^3 is the same for all the planets, as long as the same units are used for P (years, for example) and a (AU, for example).

■ If an object orbits the Sun with a semimajor axis, a, of 3 AU, what is its orbital period P_{object} in Earth years? Use Equation 3.1 and what you know about the Earth's orbit.

▨ For the object, Equation 3.1 can be written as

$$P_{object}^2 = k(a_{object})^3 = k(3 \text{ AU})^3$$
$$P_{object}^2 = k \times 27 \text{ AU}^3$$

We need to calculate a value for k. For the Earth, $a_{Earth} = 1$ AU (by definition) and $P_{Earth} = 1$ year, so for the Earth, Equation 3.1 can be written as

$$P_{Earth}^2 = k(a_{Earth})^3$$
$$(1 \text{ y})^2 = k(1 \text{ AU})^3$$
$$k = \frac{1 \text{ y}^2}{1 \text{ AU}^3}$$

In other words, $k = 1 \text{ y}^2 \text{ AU}^{-3}$. Substituting into the equation for P_{object}^2, we obtain

$$P_{object}^2 = \frac{1 \text{ y}^2}{1 \text{ AU}^3} \times 27 \text{ AU}^3$$
$$= 27 \text{ y}^2$$

$$P_{object} = \sqrt{27 \text{ y}^2}$$
$$= 5.2 \text{ y}$$

Note: $P_{object} = \sqrt{27 \text{ y}^2}$ is equivalent to $P_{object} = (27 \text{ y}^2)^{\frac{1}{2}}$

A quicker way of doing this calculation is to divide Equation 3.1 for the object by the same equation for the Earth:

$$\frac{P_{object}^2}{P_{Earth}^2} = \frac{ka_{object}^3}{ka_{Earth}^3} = \frac{(3 \text{ AU})^3}{(1 \text{ AU})^3} = \frac{27}{1}$$

therefore:

$$P_{object}^2 = 27\ P_{Earth}^2$$

$$P_{object} = \sqrt{27} \times P_{Earth} = 5.2 \text{ Earth years.}$$

Box 3.1 Using your calculator to calculate squares, cubes, square roots and cube roots

You should use a scientific calculator to calculate powers and roots similar to those in Equation 3.1. The buttons involved in these calculations will depend on the make and model of your calculator. If you already know how to do these kinds of calculations, you can ignore the rest of this box; otherwise you should work through the examples that follow, with the Instruction Manual for your calculator to hand. Most calculators have buttons that allow you to calculate squares and square roots easily.

Squares

Check that you can use your calculator to obtain the following answers:

$3^2 = 9$

$5^2 = 25$

$7^2 = 49$

■ Calculate 5.2^2 to two significant figures.

▨ $5.2^2 = 27$ to 2 significant figures.

Square roots

Check that you can use your calculator to obtain the following answers:

$\sqrt{36} = 6$ (because $6 \times 6 = 36$)

$\sqrt{64} = 8$ (because $8 \times 8 = 64$)

$\sqrt{121} = 11$ (because $11 \times 11 = 121$)

■ Calculate $\sqrt{169}$ using your calculator.

▨ $\sqrt{169} = 13$.

To work with Kepler's third law, you will also have to be able to calculate cubes and cube roots.

Cubes

Check that you can use your calculator to obtain the following answers:

$2^3 = 8$ (because $2 \times 2 \times 2 = 8$)

$3^3 = 27$

$5^3 = 125$

■ Calculate 3.5^3 using your calculator, expressing your answer to four significant figures.

▨ $3.5^3 = 42.88$.

Cube roots

Check that you can use your calculator to obtain the following answers:

$\sqrt[3]{64} = 4$ (because $4 \times 4 \times 4 = 64$)

$\sqrt[3]{216} = 6$

$\sqrt[3]{729} = 9$

Note: $\sqrt[3]{64}$ can also be written as $64^{\frac{1}{3}}$.

■ Calculate $\sqrt[3]{574}$ using your calculator, expressing your answer to three significant figures.

▨ $\sqrt[3]{574} = 8.31$ to 3 significant figures.

In addition to knowing an object's orbital period, astronomers need to know the closest and furthest points from the Sun reached by the object. For an elliptical orbit, the two points are known respectively as the perihelion and aphelion. The corresponding distances from the Sun are generally denoted by the symbols q and Q. If you look at Figure 1.3 and imagine the object at its closest and furthest points from the Sun, you will see that since these points lie at each end of the ellipse's major axis, so

$$q + Q = 2a \qquad (3.2)$$

q and Q are also related to the degree of the orbit's ellipticity (i.e. how 'squashed' it is). This is called the **eccentricity** and is denoted by the symbol e, which has no units. This relation is

$$e = \frac{Q - q}{Q + q} \qquad (3.3)$$

Where q is very small in comparison to Q, then $Q - q$ and $Q + q$ are both approximately equal to Q, so you can see that e approaches 1 for the most elliptical orbits.

■ What would e be for a circular orbit?

▨ Q and q are equal for a circle (and equal to the circle's radius), so $Q - q = 0$. 0 divided by any number is 0, so from Equation 3.3, $e = 0$.

Figure 3.1 illustrates orbits with the same semimajor axis but different eccentricities. Objects in these orbits would thus have the same orbital period but different perihelion and aphelion distances (q and Q).

Figure 3.1 Orbits around the same focus having the same semimajor axis a, but different eccentricities e, ranging from 0 (circular) to 0.9.

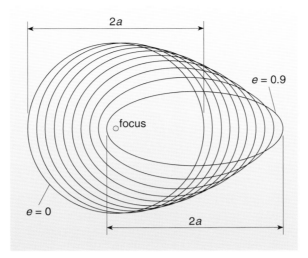

From Equations 3.2 and 3.3, q and Q can be derived in terms of a and e. First, rearranging Equation 3.3 to obtain expressions for q and Q instead of e gives:

$$q = \frac{Q(1-e)}{(1+e)} \tag{3.4}$$

and

$$Q = \frac{q(1+e)}{(1-e)} \tag{3.5}$$

Using Equation 3.4 to substitute for q in Equation 3.2 and rearranging to isolate Q yields

$$Q = a(1+e) \tag{3.6}$$

while using Equation 3.5 to substitute for Q in Equation 3.2 and rearranging to isolate q yields

$$q = a(1-e) \tag{3.7}$$

Note that when doing calculations using these equations, the distances should all have the same units (whether AU, m, km or millions of km).

So, we have seen that astronomers can describe the elliptical orbit of any Solar System body and relate it to the Sun, which lies at one of the foci of the ellipse. A series of measurements can then be used to predict the orbit of the body in the future and determine whether it will pass close to Earth.

Now we meet **Kepler's second law**, which describes the varying speed at which an object moves in its elliptical orbit. Kepler's second law states that a line connecting the Sun to a planet would sweep out equal areas of the orbital plane in equal times. While the object is far from the Sun, the distance travelled along the orbit in any particular time interval is smaller than that travelled when close to the Sun. However, the areas swept out are equal since the segment is longer when the object is further from the Sun than when it is closer, as illustrated in Figure 3.2. This is a way of quantifying the fact that objects move faster as they approach the Sun on their way round the ellipse, and move more slowly as they recede. Using this law, astronomers can calculate the speed and direction of any

Solar System body at any point in its orbital plane. This is why these mathematical equations are important; they are the basic tools that astronomers use to calculate where an asteroid will be with respect to the Sun and Earth.

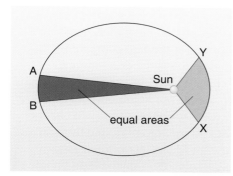

Figure 3.2 A planetary orbit illustrating Kepler's second law, which states that a planet sweeps out equal areas in equal times. Two equal areas are illustrated, showing that the planet's speed along its orbit is not uniform, but varies with its distance from the Sun. It thus travels at higher speed from X to Y than from A to B.

■ We have talked about the speed of an object in an elliptical orbit, but what happens to the speed of an object in a circular orbit?

▨ The speed remains at a constant value. Since the object's distance from the Sun is constant (the radius of its orbit), the area swept out for a given distance travelled along the circular orbit is always the same. Kepler's second law says that it must sweep out equal areas in equal times, so it must travel at a constant distance per unit time, i.e. at a constant speed.

■ Given that 1 AU is approximately 1.5×10^8 km, and the fact that the Earth has a near-circular orbit, what is the speed (km s^{-1}) at which it goes round the Sun? (*Hint*: there are 3.16×10^7 s in a year.)

▨ The circumference of a circle is $2\pi r$ (where r is the radius), so the Earth travels around $2 \times \pi \times 1.5 \times 10^8$ km y^{-1} = 9.42×10^8 km y^{-1}. Now divide by the number of seconds in a year, which gives a speed of 30 km s^{-1}.

R

Activity 3.1

Allow 1 hour

Go to Topic 2 on the S250 DVD-ROM and start the Kepler's laws activity. Open the activity notes and follow the instructions to see how orbits and orbital speeds are elucidated by Kepler's laws. Comments on the activity are included on the DVD-ROM.

Solar System bodies have orbits in three-dimensional space, but so far we have only considered two dimensions. The third dimension is important because, in general, the orbits of asteroids and comets are not in the same plane as that of the Earth – they are inclined at an angle.

To describe completely an object's position in its orbit in three dimensions – and thus communicate precisely where it is and how it is moving – requires a total of six **orbital parameters**. These are:

•   the semimajor axis

•   the eccentricity

•   the angle of inclination of the orbital plane to the **ecliptic plane** (the plane of the Earth's orbit)

53

- two angles describing where around the sky the orbital plane and major axis are pointing
- how far the object is around its orbit at a particular time.

The dynamics of elliptical orbits are governed by Kepler's laws. So-called **Keplerian orbits** assume that the body being orbited is much more massive than the body in orbit (which is a very good assumption for the Sun compared with asteroids and comets), and that the only force in action is the gravitational attraction between the two bodies. Thus the orbiting body continues going around in the same orbit *ad infinitum,* and its position is thus predictable for any time in the past or future. The reality is more complex: for instance, orbits can change when the gravitational influence of other bodies comes into play, and the orbits of comets change due to the non-gravitational, rocket-like effect of their ices **sublimating** (turning from solid into gas without going through the liquid phase) into space. These gradual changes in orbits (whether gravitational or non-gravitational in origin) are called **orbital perturbations**. As you will see later, the further into the future astronomers try to predict the orbits of asteroids and comets, the more significant these perturbations become. This is because the uncertainties associated with our measurements of orbital parameters have an ever-increasing effect on predictions further into the future.

3.3 The discovery of comets, asteroids and NEOs

For most of human history, the only Solar System bodies known in our skies, other than the Earth, were the Sun, the Moon, Mercury, Venus, Mars, Jupiter and Saturn, together with the apparently random appearance of comets. In 1510, Polish astronomer Nicolaus Copernicus (1473–1543) (following earlier Greek philosophers) put forward the idea that the Sun, rather than the Earth, lies at the centre of our Solar System. These seven celestial objects regularly visible to the unaided eye, and appearing to move against the background stars, are the reason why we have seven days in the week. Galileo Galilei (1564–1642) discovered moons orbiting Jupiter in 1610 with an early telescope. With improvements in astronomical telescopes, the fainter planets Uranus (1781), Neptune (1846) and the dwarf planet Pluto (1930) were discovered, as well as the first of the many moons of Saturn, Uranus, Neptune and Mars.

3.3.1 Comets

Although they had long been known, comets were poorly understood. Their name comes from the Greek for hair because our ancestors thought the comet tails resembled long flowing hair. It was not until Edmund Halley (1656–1742) discovered in 1705 that some historical comet apparitions occurred at regular, 76-year intervals, that multiple apparitions were attributed to a single object – now known as Halley's Comet (Figure 3.3). Like all comets, Halley has an elliptical orbit and, in this case, the orbit is retrograde (in the opposite direction to the Earth), at an inclination of around 18° to the ecliptic plane.

The familiar shape of the cometary head and tail in the sky (see Figure 3.4) occurs only when the elliptical orbit of a **comet nucleus** brings it to within a few AU of the Sun. The resultant sublimation of ices and emission of gas and dust into space is called cometary activity. Since the identification of Halley's Comet, more than 250 other **periodic comets** have been identified, with orbital periods ranging from 3.3 years to more than 350 years. Some comets have visited the inner Solar System just once in recorded history; these **long-period comets** have eccentricities very close to 1 and aphelia lying far beyond the orbit of Pluto. In fact, it is believed that there exists a spherical cloud of dormant comets at distances from about 1.0×10^4 AU to 1.0×10^5 AU. (In this context, 'dormant' means that they are too cold for any of their ices to sublimate.) Known as the Oort cloud, it is thought that these bodies formed inside the Solar System (in the region of the orbits of Uranus and Neptune) but were then ejected to great distances by close encounters with the planets. If their orbits bring them back into the inner Solar System, then we see them as comets having orbits at random angles to the ecliptic plane.

Many comets have a perihelion close to or less than 1 AU. Those with perihelia less than 1.3 AU and periods less than 200 years are classed as NEOs, or more specifically near-Earth comets (NECs). The longer-period comets are not classed as NEOs, despite the fact that some of them come close to the Earth.

■ Why do comets appear in our skies for only a few months yet have orbital periods of many years, even centuries? For example, Halley's Comet can only be seen easily using small telescopes for about 1 year of its 76-year orbit.

▨ Kepler's second law shows that comets move faster close to perihelion than around aphelion, so they move in and out of the inner Solar System in a small fraction of their orbital period. They are visible in the sky only when close enough to the Sun to be heated sufficiently to generate cometary activity (in other words, when close enough to cause sublimation of the ices into space to appear as a tail of debris).

Figure 3.3   The nucleus of Halley's Comet, as seen by the camera on the European Space Agency's Giotto spacecraft in March 1986. The nucleus, approximately 16 km × 8 km × 8 km in size, is seen surrounded by gas and dust emitted from its surface. Comet nuclei are too small to be seen from the Earth with small telescopes.

(a)

(b)

Figure 3.4   Examples of comets as observed from Earth. (a) Comet Hale-Bopp seen in 1997 and (b) Comet Hyakutake in 1996, were both naked-eye comets, i.e. they could be seen in the sky without the aid of a telescope. These images, however, were taken using a telescope. Note that in (a) the tail appears in two parts. The bluish part is called the ion tail, and is seen due to the electrically charged gas from the comet emitting light, while travelling directly away from the Sun under the influence of the solar wind. The other part is called the dust tail, and is due to light reflected and scattered from small dust particles that were ejected from the comet and are now also orbiting the Sun.

It is thought possible that some comets, having orbited close to the Sun many times, lose all their volatiles to space, leaving 'dead' comet nuclei that no longer produce gas and dust when they pass close to the Sun. This makes them indistinguishable (through telescopes at least) from certain types of asteroid.

3.3.2 Asteroids

Following the observation in the 18th century by Titius and Bode that the semimajor axes of the planets can be approximated quite closely by a simple mathematical sequence, a search was made for the 'missing planet' suggested by an 'empty slot' in the sequence between Mars and Jupiter. Whether or not the Titius–Bode 'law' has a firm physical foundation is still debated; nevertheless, an object between Mars and Jupiter was eventually discovered. However, what Giuseppe Piazzi (1746–1826) found with his telescope in 1801 was a rather faint world. It was thus not accepted as a true 'planet'. Piazzi's new world was named Ceres, after the ancient Roman grain goddess and guardian goddess of Sicily. The term asteroid was coined in 1802 by astronomer William Herschel (1738–1822) and means 'star-like' in Greek. Ceres is now known to be about 960 km in diameter. It is the largest of the smaller bodies of the inner Solar System (i.e. within the orbit of Jupiter), and in fact may now be classified as a 'dwarf planet' because its gravity is strong enough to have pulled it into a near-spherical shape. Nevertheless, many small worlds were subsequently discovered orbiting between Mars and Jupiter. By 1807 the three large asteroids named Pallas, Juno and Vesta had also been discovered; 452 asteroids were known by the end of the 19th century. The rate of discovery increased as telescopes improved and fainter objects could be distinguished. There were clearly many more smaller objects than larger ones.

It was not until the 1990s, when advanced telescopes, radar and visiting spacecraft were used, that asteroids were seen as more than points of light in the sky, revealing for the first time details such as their shapes and surface features. Only the very largest (and thus most massive) asteroids have strong enough gravity to pull themselves into a spherical shape – we thus see a wide range of irregular shapes that result from the objects' varied impact histories. Images of several asteroids and comets are included on the S250 DVD-ROM as a resource you might like to investigate.

In 1898, an asteroid was discovered whose orbit approached that of the Earth. Named Eros, the asteroid is now known to be 33 km × 13 km × 13 km in size, making it one of the largest NEOs. Many years later (in 2000–2001) it was studied at close quarters by NASA's Near-Earth Asteroid Rendezvous (NEAR–Shoemaker) mission (Figure 3.5).

The previously accepted view that asteroids orbited only between Mars and Jupiter was thus falsified. Later, in the 1930s, other asteroids were discovered whose orbits cross that of the Earth. Today, over 100 000 asteroids have been detected, of which over 30 000 have well-determined orbits. Most orbit in what is called the **Main Belt** between the orbits of Mars and Jupiter. There are so many that not all have been named, receiving instead

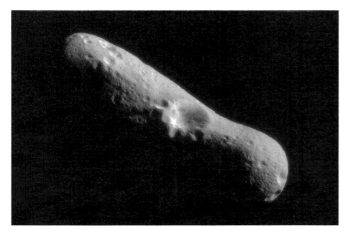

Figure 3.5   (433) Eros as seen from NEAR–Shoemaker, the first spacecraft to orbit and land on an asteroid.

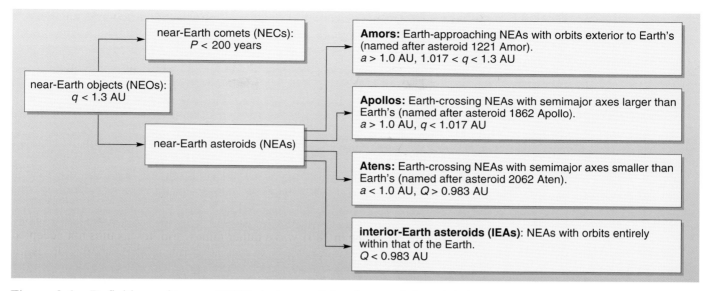

Figure 3.6   Definitions of types of NEO, in terms of the characteristics of their orbits. NEOs can be either comets (NECs) or asteroids (NEAs). Dead NECs would appear indistinguishable from NEAs, so the more general term NEOs is often used instead when discussing NEA observations. Amors, Apollos, Atens and IEAs are subgroups of NEAs. (The perihelion or aphelion limits of 1.017 AU or 0.983 AU, rather than 1.0 AU, reflect the slight eccentricity (0.017) of the Earth's orbit.)

temporary codes, including the year of discovery, for example 2004 MN4. Eventually, when their orbits become well established, they receive a permanent number and, in due course, a name can be assigned (for example 4179 Toutatis).

NEOs are subdivided into the classifications shown in Figure 3.6. The vast majority of these objects are near-Earth asteroids (NEAs); the rest are near-Earth comets (NECs). NEAs are further subdivided into four groups depending on their orbits: Amors, Apollos, Atens and interior Earth asteroids (IEAs).

■ Consider Figure 3.6. Why must the orbital period of an Amor be greater than that of an IEO?

◼ Since the orbits of Amors and IEAs lie outside and within that of the Earth, respectively, their semimajor axes must be greater than and less than 1 AU, respectively. Recalling Kepler's first law, then, Amors must have larger orbital periods than IEAs.

■ Why must the orbital period of an Apollo be greater than that of an Aten?

◼ Since the orbits of Apollos and Atens have semimajor axes greater than and less than 1.0 AU, respectively, Apollos must have larger orbital periods.

Most NEOs are not considered threatening to us, either because they never come close to the Earth or because they are thought to be too small to be hazardous. NASA's NEO Research Programme currently defines **potentially hazardous asteroids** (PHAs) as having a minimum orbit intersection distance (MOID) (i.e. closest approach to Earth) of 0.05 AU or less (which corresponds to about 7.5×10^6 km, or 20 times the Earth–Moon distance) and an **absolute magnitude** of 22 or brighter. The absolute magnitude is a measure of the brightness of an astronomical object at a standard distance, and is a quantity that can be measured (more easily than the diameter) using a telescope. A smaller value means a *brighter* object, which is somewhat counterintuitive. A magnitude increase of 5 means a brightness decrease by a factor of 100. Absolute magnitude is usually given the symbol H. An object with $H = 22$ would have a diameter between about 110 m (if it has a light, i.e. more reflective, surface) and 240 m (if it has a dark, i.e. less reflective, surface). You will read more about this effect in Section 3.5.

R

At the time of writing (2005), nearly 750 PHAs are known. This number is gradually increasing as more NEAs are discovered and tracked. The fact that an object is classed as a PHA does not mean that it *will* hit the Earth, but that there is the possibility for such a threat in the future. By monitoring the orbit of a PHA over time, the likelihood of it threatening the Earth can be assessed. It is also important to realise that the $H = 22$ limit is somewhat arbitrary, in that an object slightly less bright could still cause a lot of damage if it hit the Earth, depending on its actual mass and where it hit. Such distinctions are important when assessing the risk posed by NEOs.

The $q < 1.3$ AU limit for NEOs is also somewhat arbitrary, in that there is very little difference in the potential hazard posed by NEOs with q slightly higher than 1.3 AU than those with q just below 1.3 AU.

Figure 3.7 shows the Solar System out as far as the orbit of Jupiter, with the orbits of the inner planets and some selected asteroids and comets. Figure 3.8 shows a snapshot of the positions of asteroids relative to the orbits of the inner planets, viewed from above the ecliptic plane and from the side. You can see how most of the asteroids, but not all, are in the Main Belt and that they have a range of orbital inclinations, taking them above and below the ecliptic plane.

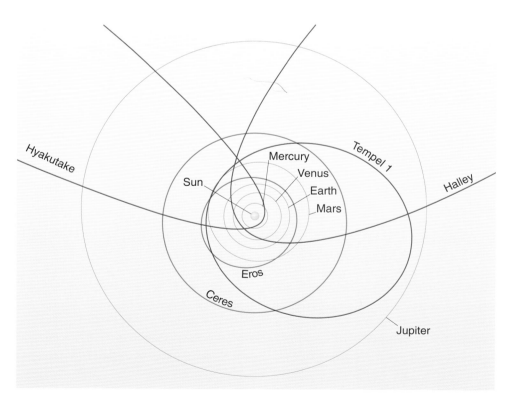

Figure 3.7   A view of the Solar System looking down on the ecliptic plane, showing the Sun and the orbits of the planets out as far as Jupiter (orange), plus the orbits of asteroids Ceres and Eros (red) and comets Halley, Hyukatake, and Tempel 1 (blue).

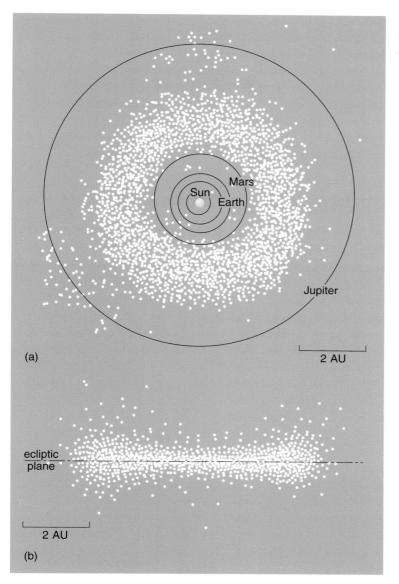

Figure 3.8 (a) Plan view and (b) side view of the inner Solar System, showing the positions of asteroids.

Asteroids and comets are believed to be the remnants of processes that formed the planets some 4550 million years ago from a large cloud of gas and dust orbiting the Sun. While most of this primordial (meaning ancient and unmodified) material accumulated, through gravitational attraction and collisions, into larger and larger pieces to form the planets, some remained as smaller fragments. In the warm, inner Solar System these fragments comprised rocky material, while in the outer Solar System the fragments also contained material too volatile to condense closer to the Sun. This material includes water ice and the solid forms of other chemicals that would be gases or liquids on Earth, such as carbon monoxide (CO) and ammonia (NH_3). Comets are believed to contain icy material that has been in cold storage in the outer Solar System for most of its history, only 'recently' having been drawn into the inner Solar System by gravitational perturbations (by Jupiter, for example). Asteroids, too, have been subjected to modification since the early history of the Solar System. Some are known to have formed at an early stage into bodies large enough for internal heat and gravity to separate gradually the denser, metallic material such as iron and nickel (which falls towards the centre) from the lighter, rocky material (which floats to the surface). This process is called **differentiation** and happened to all the planets and larger moons. Collisions between asteroids have cratered their surfaces and broken larger bodies into smaller ones. Meteorites that fall to the surface of the Earth are evidence for this, and their diversity reflects the range of bodies from which they originated – not from a single, 'failed' planet but from many small bodies that never accreted to form a planet. Before they hit the Earth, the meteorites collected at the Earth's surface can in fact be considered as small NEOs.

3.4 Impact probabilities and uncertainties

R

Tracking a newly discovered asteroid across the sky enables its orbital parameters to be calculated using Kepler's laws, albeit with some finite uncertainty that decreases as more observations are included in the calculations. If an asteroid is predicted to have a close approach to the Earth at some point in the future, the likelihood of it actually hitting the Earth at that time is quantified by means of a **probability** and is given the symbol p. This is a number between 0 (definitely will not happen) and 1 (definitely will happen). As an example, if $p = 0.001$ for an asteroid to collide with the Earth on a particular close approach, then this means a probability of one in a thousand of a collision occurring. For the vast majority of known NEOs, p is known to be zero, or very nearly so, for close approaches to the Earth for at least the next century. As the accuracy of an orbit prediction improves, p for a particular close approach changes. The value of p can vary both up and down, but eventually reaches either 0 or (far less likely) 1. This variation in the value of p as more data are gathered and predictions improve has been one source of controversy when communicating the NEO risk between scientists and to the public. As you will see in Chapter 4, objects for which a few observations might indicate a significant probability of impact with Earth can, a few days later, have their impact probability reduced to zero. From the standpoint of someone outside the professional astronomy community, it might look as though the scientists 'got it wrong' with the previous, non-zero probability. The following activity explores the way that the predicted probability changes as more data are added.

C R

Activity 3.2

Allow about 2 hours

Go to Topic 2 on the S250 DVD-ROM and start the impact probability calculator. Open the activity notes and follow the instructions to see how observations of NEOs are used to predict impacts on the Earth. Comments on the activity are included on the DVD-ROM.

As you will have seen in Activity 3.2, it is not just the number of data points available that determines the quality of the prediction. Just a few extra isolated points from earlier observations can reduce the uncertainty in the prediction dramatically. In several important cases, a 'newly' discovered asteroid had actually been detected by chance years earlier, in photographs or CCD images of the sky taken either for other reasons or as part of an asteroid search/tracking project, but which the detection had been indistinct. These **prediscovery** (so-called 'precovery') observations are important for improving the predictions of an NEO's orbit, but often take some time to research, creating a delay in their reporting to other astronomers and the general public.

Plotting the orbital parameters of many asteroids shows that they are not smoothly distributed over a range of values, but that there are several sizes, shapes and orientations of orbit for which there are few if any asteroids. As an example, Figure 3.9 shows eccentricity *e* plotted against semimajor axis *a* for the known asteroid population. The main feature of the plot is the cluster of points between about 1.8 AU and 3.2 AU, corresponding to the Main Belt. However, within this you can see a number of gaps, particularly at around 2.1 AU and 2.5 AU. These gaps are the result of gravitational perturbations, caused particularly by Jupiter. Any object straying into that region is subjected to repeated small 'tugs' from the giant planet that either accelerates or decelerates the object, throwing its orbit out of the gap. These gaps in the distribution of orbits are known as **unstable resonances**. Scattering of objects from such unstable resonances is believed to be the main way in which asteroids in the Main Belt are transferred into the inner Solar System to become NEOs.

Today, some 4550 million years after the origin of the Solar System, there are still numerous asteroids that could collide with the Earth. The lifetimes of these asteroids must be short relative to the age of the Solar System because they are 'rapidly' removed by collisions with the terrestrial planets. It is believed that **orbital evolution** of asteroids in the Main Belt results in a continuous supply to the inner Solar System, thus replenishing the NEO population.

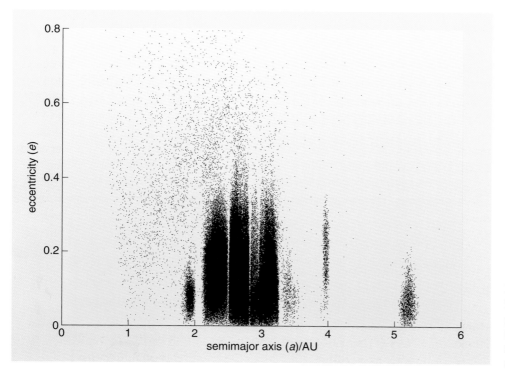

Figure 3.9   Plot of *e* versus *a* for the asteroid population. The gaps at about 2.1 AU and 2.5 AU are thought to be the unstable resonances that supply about 60% of the NEO population.

Changes in an object's orbital parameters are known as orbital evolution. An asteroid's orbit can also change suddenly if it has a close encounter with a planet. In such cases, the planet's gravitational pull changes the direction of the asteroid as it passes by, putting it into a different orbit. This is the same effect that is used by some interplanetary spacecraft to change speed and direction 'for free', enabling them to reach their destinations using less rocket fuel. For example, in December 2000 the Cassini/Huygens spacecraft used such a **gravity assist** encounter with Jupiter to sling it out towards its final destination, the Saturnian system, where it finally released the Huygens probe to fall to the surface of Titan in January 2005 (Figure 3.10).

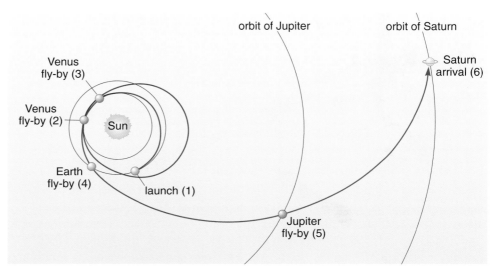

Figure 3.10 Trajectory of the Cassini/Huygens spacecraft, showing its trajectory from launch in October 1997 (1) and the gravity assists from Venus (2, 3), the Earth (4) and Jupiter (5) before arriving at Saturn (6) in July 2004.

Gravitational perturbations are just one reason why astronomers cannot predict orbits far into the future. Non-gravitational influences cause orbital evolution and, over long time periods, these very weak forces play an important role. These forces include the tiny pressure exerted by sunlight falling on the surfaces of asteroids and the infrared light emitted from their surfaces. The physics of this effect, called radiation pressure, is beyond the scope of this course; all you need to know is that such small effects may accumulate over time. These effects are sometimes amplified by close encounters with planets, the outcomes of which are very sensitive to the orbital parameters. The small perturbations sometimes make the difference between an NEO being put into a threatening orbit by a close encounter and it remaining in a safe orbit. Collisions between NEOs are another way in which their orbits can change. Such events happen rarely to any particular NEO, however.

Perturbations need to be taken into account when predicting the orbits of asteroids (or, indeed, working backwards in time to determine where they came from). In this respect, the Solar System can no longer be thought of like a clockwork orrery (Figure 3.11) – with bodies travelling endlessly round their fixed orbits – but rather as a cosmic shooting gallery, with the ever-changing orbiting swarm of small bodies.

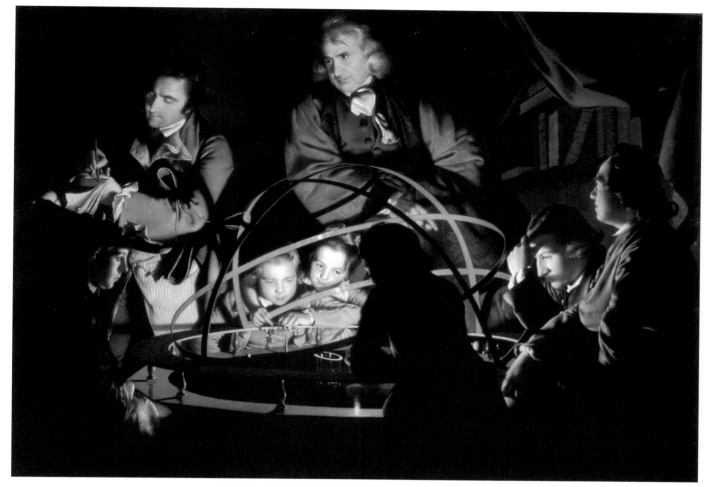

Figure 3.11   Portrayal of an orrery in art. Models of the planets and their moons move round circular orbits by means of a clockwork mechanism. *A philosopher lecturing on the orrery*, Joseph Wright of Derby, exhibited 1766. Oil on canvas, 1473 mm × 2032 mm.

3.5 NEO astronomical observations and population

When seen through a telescope, asteroids appear as star-like points of light, but what scientists need to know in order to estimate their danger in an impact with Earth is the size and density of each object and thus its mass. In addition, in order to estimate the overall risk to Earth from the whole NEO population, scientists need an estimate of how many NEOs there are of each size so astronomers can calculate how many remain to be found.

3.5.1 Astronomical observations

The diversity of asteroids is clear even from telescopic observations, which can be made using filters to measure the object's brightness in visible and infrared (longer wavelength than visible) light. Taking into account variations due to the angle from which the Sun is shining relative to the line from the Earth to the

R

asteroid (things are easier to see when the Sun is directly behind the observer) and the distance of the asteroid (things further away are fainter), objects that appear brighter are only *on average* likely to be larger. Uncertainties in the determination of size result from the possible range of surface reflectivity, or **albedo**, exhibited by different objects. This is the reason why all sizes assigned to asteroids of a particular absolute magnitude are, if no additional data are available, rather uncertain. Clearly, even when an object is found by astronomers, its size is not easy to estimate and there is a great deal more work to do before its threat can be assessed with precision.

The light from an asteroid detected by a telescope is a mixture of reflected sunlight and infrared radiation emitted as a result of its surface temperature. When an object is heated, it emits electromagnetic radiation with a range of wavelengths that depend on its temperature. For example, an iron bar heated in a blacksmith's forge glows orange. At temperatures similar to those on the Earth's surface – or that of an asteroid – infrared light is emitted with wavelengths of around 10^{-5} m. You may have seen images from satellite-based remote sensing that make use of this phenomenon. Two objects that both appear, say, green to us could be clearly distinguished if they were emitting different amounts of infrared radiation. This effect is also very useful in distinguishing small, light-coloured asteroids from larger, darker ones that when seen through a telescope (in visible light) would appear to be very similar. In other words, the larger, darker object would be warmer and radiate more thermal infrared than the smaller, lighter object. This is illustrated in Figure 3.12.

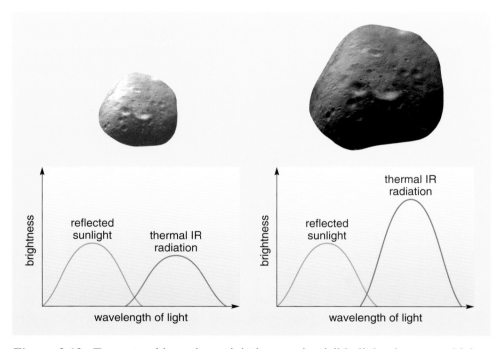

Figure 3.12 Two asteroids as they might be seen in visible light close up, which would be just points of light of similar brightness when seen through a telescope on Earth. The one on the left is smaller but has a higher albedo, so reflects the same amount of light as the larger, darker one on the right. The larger, darker one shows more emission in the thermal infrared, however, because it presents a larger surface area towards the observer.

Measurements of an asteroid's brightness at different wavelengths – its colour – carry information about its surface composition. This gives an approximate indication of the asteroid composition, for example whether it is rocky, metallic or primitive (i.e. undifferentiated). This depends on where its material originally formed and what thermal, physical and chemical processes have occurred since. Many different 'colour families', known as **spectral types**, of asteroids have been identified. Asteroids of each spectral type show spectra that are similar and distinguishable from other spectral types.

It would be ideal to know the size and spectral type of every asteroid discovered. This is not possible from a practical point of view, however, due to the sheer number of asteroids identified and the specialised, time-consuming observations required for such measurements. For most asteroids, all that is known are the orbit (with some degree of uncertainty) and absolute magnitude. Other properties are known only for the small fraction of (generally larger) objects that have so far been studied in more detail.

In order to know how much kinetic energy an NEO would have if it hit the Earth, and thus how much destruction it might cause, it is necessary to know both its mass and speed (see Equation 1.1). The speed with which it would impact depends on the direction and speed of its orbit in relation to that of the Earth at the time of impact, as well as the extra speed gained as it is pulled by Earth's gravity. The masses of only a few asteroids are known, however. Those that are known are mostly cases where the asteroid's gravity has a measurable effect on the motion of something we can observe, such as a moon of its own (called a 'binary companion'), a spacecraft or another asteroid.

For the vast majority of cases, however, the mass can only be estimated by multiplying its estimated volume V by an estimated bulk density ρ:

$$m = V \times \rho \tag{3.8}$$

Sizes, and thus volumes, can be determined by telescopic observations, spacecraft imagery or radar. Densities of asteroids are believed to range from around 1300 kg m^{-3} for some porous asteroids, to at least 3500 kg m^{-3} for metallic asteroids. The density of stony asteroids lies between these extremes, at around 2500 kg m^{-3}. Comets are thought to have low densities, perhaps around 800 kg m^{-3}.

■   Given that water ice has a density of 917 kg m^{-3}, how can an icy comet nucleus have a density that is less than this value?

▨   Such a comet nucleus would have to be porous, that is to say contain a proportion of empty space within its volume.

So, the density depends not just on the material from which an NEO is made, but also on how much porosity it has. Some asteroids are thought to comprise fragments that have come back together again under their own weak gravity, following an impact event, to form a loosely bound 'rubble pile' that contains a significant proportion of empty space in the interior.

You saw in Chapter 1 that one of the most important parameters in judging the hazard from an NEO is the kinetic energy of the body, which depends upon both its mass and its speed. Mass in turn depends on the radius and density of the

R

asteroid and, while astronomical observations can estimate radius, density is beyond such measurements. However, astronomers can still achieve reasonable estimates of the risk posed by a given body because, while radius might vary by many orders of magnitude (from a few tens of metres to hundreds of kilometres), density probably only varies from 1300 kg m^{-3} to 3500 kg m^{-3}, a factor of about 2.7. Thus, an underestimate of the density could potentially produce an underestimate of the kinetic energy by a factor of no more than about 3.

■ Two asteroids have been spotted: one is travelling at 10 km s^{-1} and the other is travelling twice as fast. However, the faster asteroid (asteroid 1) is estimated to be 500 m in radius, which is half the radius of the slower asteroid (2). Using Equation 1.1, calculate which asteroid has the greater kinetic energy. Assume they are spherical (the volume of a sphere $= \frac{4}{3}\pi r^3$) and have the same density, 2500 kg m^{-3}. Finally, explain which is the more important parameter in determining the kinetic energy of an asteroid: speed or radius.

▨ Combining Equation 1.1 and Equation 3.8 (by substituting $V\rho$ for m in Equation 1.1):

$$E_k = \frac{1}{2}V\rho v^2$$

$$E_{\text{asteroid 1}} = 0.5\left[\frac{4}{3}\times 3.142\,(500\text{ m})^3\right]\times 2500\text{ kg m}^{-3}\times(20\,000\text{ m s}^{-1})^2$$

$$= 2.5\times 10^{20}\text{ J}$$

$$E_{\text{asteroid 2}} = 0.5\left[\frac{4}{3}\times 3.142\,(1000\text{ m})^3\right]\times 2500\text{ kg m}^{-3}\times(10\,000\text{ m s}^{-1})^2$$

$$= 5.3\times 10^{20}\text{ J}$$

The asteroid that was twice the radius of the other has more than twice the kinetic energy, even though it was travelling only half as fast. Clearly, radius is the most important parameter when calculating the kinetic energy of asteroids (because the radius is cubed in the equation for volume).

In addition to telescopes and spacecraft, radar has also been used to observe and investigate asteroids that have been discovered previously by other means. Rather than measuring the visible or infrared light naturally reflected or emitted from asteroids, radio waves are bounced off the asteroid. The time delay is used to determine the distance to the asteroid, and the strength and **Doppler** frequency shift of the echoes are measured. The Doppler effect is the change in wavelength (or frequency) of a wave as received by an observer, due to the motion of the source (or reflector) along the line of sight from the receiver. Motion towards the observer causes an increase in the received frequency and motion away from the observer causes a decrease. This effect can be heard (for sound waves rather than light) when a siren on a fast-moving vehicle goes past the listener.

From a series of radar echoes, an asteroid's orbit and shape can be measured very accurately, allowing more accurate predictions of its future orbit to be made. Figure 3.13 shows a radar image of asteroid Toutatis, obtained in December 1992 using the Goldstone radar in California. A sequence of such images can be used to produce a 'shape model' showing surface features.

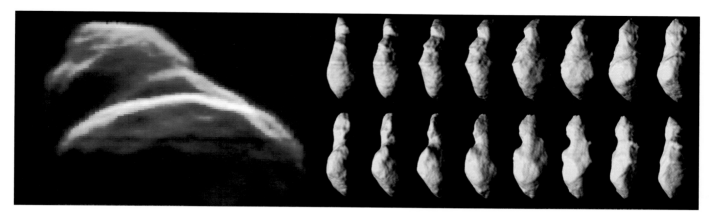

Figure 3.13 Radar image of asteroid (4179) Toutatis (that you first saw in Figure 1.1) obtained by the Goldstone radar in California in 1992 (left), and a shape model created using a sequence of radar images (right). It is 1.9 km × 2.3 km × 4.6 km in size.

3.5.2 The population of NEOs and the risk of Earth impact

R

Although most astronomical observations are unable to provide direct determinations of the density and size of individual asteroids, classifying each discovery in terms of its magnitude (brightness), position and spectral type allows scientists to make an estimation of density and size. This is enhanced by combining many observations and examining the statistics of the NEO population. Using the database of asteroids discovered so far, and information and knowledge of the impact rates on the Earth and Moon, several groups of scientists have estimated the total number of NEAs greater than 1 km diameter. It is thought that the population is static; for example as asteroids hit planets, fall into the Sun or are ejected from the inner Solar System, their number is being constantly replenished from the Main Belt of asteroids. The constant replenishment, as we saw above, is the result of perturbations caused by Jupiter's gravity. The method of estimating the total population is quite involved because there are several known sources of bias in the data, including the fact that only certain areas of the sky have been searched. However, there is reasonable agreement on the numbers involved.

One of the first observations is that smaller NEAs are much more common than larger NEAs. This is shown graphically in Figure 3.14 as a plot of the number of objects larger than a given diameter against diameter. The numbers of NEAs range from only a few that are larger than 10 km in diameter to more than 10 000 that are larger than 200 m. The plot uses a logarithmic rather than a linear scale so the smaller diameter asteroids are not crammed up against the axes and difficult to see. The margin of uncertainty is estimated by considering the likely range and taking into account the assumptions made, for example regarding albedo.

The curve is corrected for **observational bias**; fewer objects have been discovered than are indicated in the plot, especially towards the smaller end of the size scale (smaller ones are more difficult to find). Since they have not yet been discovered, a prediction has to be made to produce the line shown. Such predictions are based on a range of considerations, including the known capabilities of search efforts and the rate at which new objects are discovered. The curve continues to even smaller sizes. Sizes below about 10 m are considered as meteoroids rather than NEAs and these are the bodies that reach the Earth's surface as meteorites, some of which are recovered by humans. The rate at which these fall to Earth can be used as another check at the smaller end of the NEA population.

Dedicated NEA detection and tracking efforts use ground-based telescopes to try to discover and track as many as possible of the NEAs above a certain size. There are several collaborative projects searching for NEAs; currently one of their main aims is to reach NASA's 'Spaceguard Goal', which is to find 90% of the NEAs larger than 1 km diameter by 2008.

R

■ The 1 km limit was designed partly because that was what astronomers believed might be achieved in the time. Given your knowledge of the approximate size of the body that caused the Barringer Crater, will the achievement of this goal end all worries about NEAs?

▨ The body that formed the Barringer Crater was less than 100 m in diameter, so the current Spaceguard effort only addresses the largest impactors, those which might form craters tens of kilometres across.

One of the aims of estimating the NEA population is to recognise when the goal is reached. At the time of writing (2005) the best estimate of the population greater than 1 km diameter is 1090 ± 180 (that is to say it has a 1-sigma likelihood (68%) of being between $1090 - 180$ and $1090 + 180$, which is between 910 and 1270). There are probably no more than about 80 NECs.

Another way of thinking about the impacts of different-sized bodies on Earth is to consider the average time interval between impacts of a particular size or larger (Figure 3.15). This time interval depends on the flux (that is to say the number arriving per unit area per second) of objects from the NEA population at the location of the Earth and also the size of the Earth. The curve is thus closely related to the asteroid size distribution in Figure 3.14. This is because the smaller and more numerous asteroids arrive more frequently. Figure 3.15 shows this distribution, once again using a log–log scale. From the data on NEA populations it is possible to calculate that the average interval between globally destructive impacts by asteroids around 1 km in diameter is 0.6 ± 0.1 million years. Regionally destructive impacts (~200 m diameter asteroids) strike the Earth every $56\,000 \pm 6000$ years; and finally, impacts such as Tunguska occur every 2000–3000 years. Again, the ranges reflect the uncertainties associated with these quantities.

■ The Barringer Crater formed 50 000 years ago and, according to the estimates of reoccurrence, such events happen every 56 000 years. Should we relax for the next few thousand years?

▨ No, NEO impacts occur randomly. This is the average time between impacts, not a prediction of the time of impact.

This impact frequency distribution shows that it is possible to assess the threat, though it does not predict precisely when the next impact will occur. The

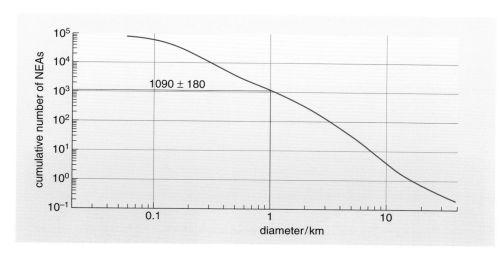

Figure 3.14 Cumulative numbers of NEAs versus NEA diameter. (Refer back to Figure 1.4 for explanations of log scale.)

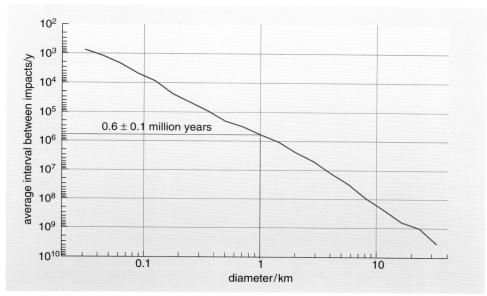

Figure 3.15 Average time interval between impacts versus NEA diameter. (Note that the interval decreases going up the vertical axis.)

detection of threatening asteroids, by means of astronomical observations that detect and track NEAs, is the only way to assess whether any particular member of this population poses a threat or not. By searching in a coordinated and collaborative manner, humans have a good chance of identifying the next threatening object before it hits the Earth. Such an early warning would allow, at least in principle, space technology to be used to combat the threat, either by destroying or diverting the object. Such possibilities and the challenges involved will be discussed in more detail towards the end of Chapter 4.

You should note that the current search is aimed at asteroids whose whole orbit is within the inner Solar System. Advance warning may not be possible in the case of long-period comets, however, since they are seen for the first time only when they become active on their way into the inner Solar System. Estimates of the hazard from the long-period comet population place it between 1% and 10% of that from the NEA population, so they are less important to the current search. Although long-period comets are not classed as NEAs, they do pose a threat, mostly through large, very rare impacts.

R

Finally, research into the morphology and composition of asteroids is moving forward rapidly, partly as the result of space missions. One of the results is that asteroids are now known to have moons or satellites (smaller asteroids) in orbit around them. The first of these was seen by the Galileo spacecraft as it flew past the asteroid (243) Ida in 1993. A small companion, now named Dactyl (Figure 3.16), was seen in the images. It now seems that such binary asteroids are more common than had previously been thought.

Figure 3.16 (243) Ida (56 km × 24 km × 21 km) and Dactyl (1.2 km × 1.4 km × 1.6 km), as seen by the Galileo spacecraft, with a close-up of Dactyl.

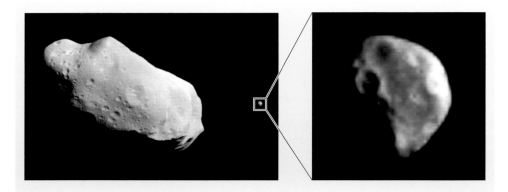

In addition, the NEAR–Shoemaker spacecraft ended its mission to (433) Eros in February 2001 by descending to the surface, thus performing the first ever landing on a small body. Figure 3.17 shows the final images it took just before it touched down. Eros is one of the largest NEAs and scientists are now able to decipher more of its history by examining the craters, boulders and dust on the surface. A number of further asteroid missions are either underway, for example the Japanese Mission to (25143) Itokawa, or planned, to perform a host of measurements to characterise their composition and structure and even to bring samples back to Earth for analysis and comparison with meteorites.

5 m

Figure 3.17 Mosaic of the last four images obtained by NEAR–Shoemaker during its descent to the surface of (433) Eros in 2001.

Summary of Chapter 3

1   Kepler's second law states that a line connecting the Sun to a planet would sweep out equal areas of space in equal times. This relationship describes how the speed of an object varies on the way around its orbit.

2   Kepler's third law states that the square of a planet's orbital period is proportional to the cube of the length of its semimajor axis. This relationship allows astronomers to calculate the time taken for an asteroid to perform a complete orbit.

3   The orbit of an object in space can be uniquely defined by six parameters: the semimajor axis, eccentricity, inclination, the two angles describing the orientation of the orbital plane, and the object's position in its orbit. NEO orbital parameters can change due to perturbations.

4   The population of NEOs is constantly replenished via orbital evolution from the main asteroid belt, due largely to unstable resonances with Jupiter.

5   NEOs can be categorised into several groups, including NECs, NEAs, Amors, Apollos, Atens, IEAs and PHAs, based on their orbits. Long-period comets also pose a hazard but are not classed as NEOs.

6   All orbits based on observations have an inherent uncertainty. This translates into uncertainty as to whether they will ever impact Earth.

7   Orbital calculations are often improved after their initial discovery by data that might have been gathered months or even years earlier.

8   Estimates of the size and mass of asteroids are based on optical characteristics and are also subject to uncertainty. Two asteroids with the same size but different albedos might be assigned different sizes based on their optical characteristics; this can be resolved using thermal IR observations. The energy of an impact depends on the NEO's size, density and speed relative to the Earth.

9   The population of NEOs has been estimated based upon observations up to the present day, combined with evidence from craters on the surface of the Moon. There are thought to be around 1090 ± 180 NEOs larger than 1 km in diameter. Objects this size or larger hit the Earth on average once every 0.6 ± 0.1 million years.

Questions for Chapter 3

Question 3.1

Mars has a semimajor axis of 1.52 AU. Using Equation 3.1, calculate the length of the Martian year P_{Mars} in Earth days.

Question 3.2

What are the orbital period and eccentricity of Pluto's orbit, given that its semimajor axis is 39.48 AU, its perihelion is 29.65 AU and its aphelion is 49.31 AU?

Question 3.3

Each of the four orbit diagrams in Figure 3.18 shows the orbit of the Earth (black) and the orbit of an NEA in the same plane. The four diagrams illustrate orbits for each of the four NEA subgroups Amors, Apollos, Atens and IEAs. Identify the correct subgroup of NEA represented by each of the red orbits in Figure 3.18a–d.

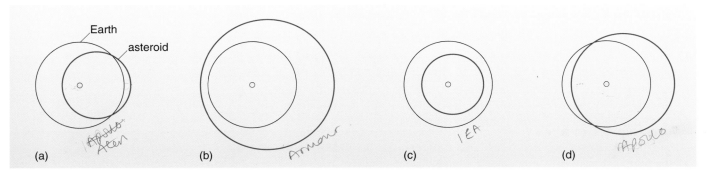

Figure 3.18 Plan view of the orbits of four asteroids (in purple) together with the Earth's orbit (in black).

Question 3.4

The principle of conservation of energy must be valid for orbiting Solar System bodies. Using kinetic energy (energy possessed by a body because of its motion) and potential energy (energy possessed by a body because of its position), briefly explain how the type of energy changes as a body travels along an orbit around the Sun, such as that shown in Figure 1.3b.

Chapter 4

The social context of the impact hazard

This chapter will look at society's perception of the risk of an NEO impact, the response to this low-probability natural hazard with potentially catastrophic consequences, and moves by decision makers to address the problem. In addition, you will consider how scientists have striven to communicate the risk of an NEO impact to the public without being accused of either covering up or exaggerating the hazard. Finally, the advances made by the Spaceguard Survey, and some of the possibilities for diverting or destroying a threatening NEO using space technology, will be discussed.

C R E D

Activity 4.1 (Part 1)

On-going

As you have seen, we are using icons in the margins to draw your attention to material that is particularly relevant to one or more of the course themes of communication, risk, ethical issues and decision making. However, as you progress through the course, you should increasingly be able to identify passages that relate to the themes without the help of these icons.

In the first book on BSE/vCJD, you were asked to note passages of text particularly relevant to ethical issues. In the rest of this chapter, we will use the icons for communication, risk, and ethical issues – but not for decision making. Instead, you should write the letter D in the margin adjacent to the text that you consider to be particularly relevant to decision making. You should also make brief notes to remind yourself of the way(s) you consider the material to be relevant. We will return to this activity at the end of the chapter.

4.1 Asteroids and the rise of neo-catastrophism

Astrologers held sway over interpretation of the heavens until the end of the 17th century, and **astronomers** had been frustrated by failed attempts to explain the irregular orbital motions of the planets. The Scientific Revolution brought an end to this worrying uncertainty as Isaac Newton's (1643–1727) mathematical explanation of planetary orbits enabled astronomers to calculate the orbits and future whereabouts of the planets.

C R

It is interesting to note here that Newton solved the mathematical problems required to prove Kepler's laws but did not immediately publish his work. No one knew of his breakthrough until Edmond Halley visited him in Cambridge to discuss his own (Halley's) ideas on Kepler's laws. When Halley realised the enormity of Newton's advance, he convinced the latter to publish the work, which appeared as the *Principia Mathematica Philosophiae Naturalis* (1687) and was published at Halley's expense. Edmond Halley was a brilliant scientist in

C R

his own right and plays an important role in two other parts of the NEO story. He made the first prediction of an NEC approach (as we saw in Chapter 3) when he predicted that a comet seen in 1682 would return in 1758. Halley also made an important contribution to actuarial science (which we met in Chapter 1). In 1693 he published an article on methods of calculating the price of life annuities (life insurance), based on his analysis of long-term records of age-at-death. Halley's work allowed the government to sell life annuities priced according to the age of the purchaser, and strongly influenced the development of actuarial science.

Ever since Newton, we have learned to see our Universe through the lens of order and stability. In this deeply ingrained view, the world works like a giant clockwork orrery (Figure 3.11) according to a set of universal laws that can be recognised and understood. In fact, perhaps the greatest triumph of Newtonian **cosmology** was the scientific explanation of the movement of comets which had until that time appeared in the heavens for reasons beyond understanding. At the time, the ability to understand the movement of both the planets and comets laid to rest the ancestral fear of comets as portents or omens of future events or a judgmental God.

The main message of this new cosmology was that human society could be assured of the constancy, predictability and stability of our world. The 18th century optimism of the scientific 'Enlightenment' assured European society (which had been habitually alarmed about cometary apparitions) that the universe ran without divine interventions or heavenly disasters.

C R   In the early 19th century, a new class of extraterrestrial bodies, namely asteroids, was detected. Ceres, the first asteroid, was discovered by Giuseppe Piazzi in 1801, as you saw in Chapter 3. Once astronomers realised that interplanetary space contained small objects that were orbiting the Sun, it became reasonable to suggest that asteroids may have collided with the Earth or the Moon in the past – and may do so again in the future. The first suggestions that the lunar craters had been produced by asteroid impacts were published as early as 1802 and 1815. However, these proposals did not receive wide circulation or attention, since asteroids were not regarded as a real risk to the Earth. The asteroids discovered during the 19th century lay overwhelmingly in orbits that were confined to the space between the orbits of Mars and Jupiter (Figures 3.8 and 3.9). Since they displayed near-circular orbits and were thus highly predictable, their discovery prompted no anxiety.

C R   It was not until the 20th century that it became clear that the orbits of some objects intersected the Earth's orbit and brought them close to our planet (Figure 1.2b). In addition, despite the fact that it was predicted, the return of Halley's Comet in 1910 still unnerved some people. Although the state of scientific knowledge was sufficiently advanced that any risk from the comet could be dismissed, the unsupported fear was that the comet tail, through which the Earth was due to pass, contained poisonous gases. Some people sealed their windows, and one businessman made a fortune from sales of 'comet pills', which were supposed to be an antidote to the poisonous gases.

■ Which incident described in Chapter 1 shows a similar gulf between scientific comprehension and public perception? What factor connects these two events?

▨ There are strong similarities between the reaction of some to Halley's Comet in 1910 and the public panic surrounding *The War of the Worlds* radio broadcast in 1938. Both incidents were caused by unfounded scares that could have been dismissed had the information been disseminated (and believed) in sufficient time.

In the 1930s, the first so-called Apollo asteroids (i.e. asteroids that cross the Earth's path) were discovered (see Figure 3.6). Gradually, the Earth-threatening orbits of some asteroids started to undermine the notion of a safe cosmos, and the perception that disorder rather than harmony held sway in the Solar System began to emerge.

During the 20th century, the shift that led to the gradual replacement of the concept of an essentially benign universe by that of an unpredictable cosmos, punctuated by cosmic catastrophes, occurred in several phases. One of the notable incidents occurred in 1927, when Leonid Kulik, a Russian scientist, announced that he had discovered a large historical NEO impact. Kulik confirmed that he had detected the devastated area resulting from an NEO impact near the Tunguska river in Siberia in 1908 (referred to in Chapters 1 and 2). However, despite the rather spectacular report, only a handful of individuals were interested in the search for extraterrestrial debris or the craters that some of them had left behind. Harvey Nininger, the founder of the scientific study of meteorites, tried in vain to convince the scientific world to finance a US expedition to Tunguska.

■ Which discovery later in the 20th century demonstrated the enormous potential of NEOs to threaten life on the Earth?

▨ The discovery that 65 million years ago an NEO impact caused a 170 km crater at Chicxulub in Mexico, and contributed to a mass extinction of life on Earth.

The first modern asteroid scare, when for a short while scientists realised for the first time that an asteroid was approaching close to the Earth, occurred in late October 1937. A newly discovered object, asteroid (69230) Hermes, passed so close to Earth that leading astronomers at the time even contemplated its collision with Earth (Box 4.1).

C

Box 4.1 The world's first asteroid scare

Sunday Graphic (London), November 1937

WORLD DISASTER MISSED – BY 5 HOURS

Scientists watch a planet hurtling earthward

The Earth has just escaped disaster and possibly destruction in a collision with another planet by five and a half hours. Astronomers in England and South Africa are the witnesses.

'It was the nearest thing to a collision between the Earth and another body that has ever happened,' said Dr H.E. Wood, South African astronomer, in Cape Town yesterday. He revealed that he and 30 other Cape astronomers had watched the phenomenon.

On October 25 a minor planet was first seen to be rushing through space, making for the Earth in a straight line. As the days passed it was obvious that if the planet missed us it would only be by an astronomical fraction. Finally it shot past the Earth, 400,000 miles and five and a half hours away – a small astronomical distance.

English astronomers who also observed the phenomenon spoke guardedly, but they agreed yesterday that the world had the narrowest escape ever recorded. Mr William M.H. Graves, one of the two secretaries of the Royal Astronomical Society, told the *Sunday Graphic*: 'According to our observations, it was about 600,000 miles away at its nearest position. Shortly before the war [First World War] a big meteor fell in a deserted region of Siberia and damaged several hundred square miles…'

What if the little asteroid Hermes had struck lower New York last October—that would have been the end of the world for millions of people in the great skyscrapers of the metropolitan area and for ships in the harbor. Drawing by Walter Favreau

Figure 4.1 Artist's impression in *Sky & Telescope* magazine of an NEO impact at the time of the Hermes close approach.

■ How does the journalist of the article emphasise uncertainty concerning the Hermes close encounter?

C

▨ The uncertainty is heightened by quoting different groups of scientists who have apparently different views. In this case the South African group emphasise the closeness of the approach, while the English astronomers play down the risk by referring to another known incident in Siberia. The distances of closest approach estimated by the two groups appear different but, as you saw in Chapter 3, the uncertainty in the observations probably meant that the two estimates overlapped.

As a direct result of the Hermes close encounter, Nininger suggested in 1942 that some episodes of mass extinction in the geological record may have been the consequence of past NEO collisions with the Earth. Nininger was not the first to suggest that catastrophes have played a major role in the history of life on Earth; as long ago as 1750, French astronomer Pierre Louis de Maupertuis (1698–1759) suggested that comets struck the Earth and killed off life 'en masse', but the hypothesis failed to gain widespread support.

C R

Perhaps the reason why so few paid attention to the impact hypothesis was that the main basis of scientists' understanding of the Earth system is **uniformitarianism**, the paradigm first espoused by James Hutton (1726–1797) and developed by Charles Lyell (1797–1875). In short, uniformitarianism holds that 'the present is the key to the past'; in other words, the best way to understand processes in the past is to study present-day processes. However, **catastrophism** began to re-emerge after more than a century of uniformitarian dominance as **neo-catastrophism** (the concept that high-magnitude events played an important role in the evolution of life on Earth). Images of impact craters and lunar rocks sent back by space missions in the 1960s and 1970s exposed the pock-marked, impact-covered surface of many planets. At the same time, the identification of high-speed meteorite impact craters on the Earth helped to generate a new view of our planet as a fundamentally hazardous place experiencing the same history as other bodies in the Solar System. It was not until the early 1980s, however, with the discovery of the K/T impact boundary layer, that the scientific community accepted the reality of long-term bombardment by asteroids and comets (Chapter 2).

C R

It was during this crucial period of the 1960s and 1970s that asteroid (1566) Icarus was expected to make a close approach to Earth on 14 June 1968, at a miss distance of 0.042 AU.

■ Did the asteroid Icarus pass closer to the Earth than the distance between the Earth and the Moon? The distance from the Earth to the Sun is 1 AU or around 1.5×10^8 km, and the average distance between the Earth and the Moon is 382 500 km.

▨ The ratio of the Earth–Moon and Earth–Sun distances (382 500/150 000 000) is also the Earth–Moon distance in astronomical units because the Earth–Sun distance is 1 AU. Thus the Moon is 0.00255 AU from the Earth. So if the asteroid passed 0.042 AU from the Earth, its closest approach was at a distance around 16.5 times the Earth–Moon distance.

C   This 1968 incident was the first time that an asteroid had been observed and its orbit measured, allowing astronomers to predict a close approach to Earth. The predicted close approach triggered great international media attention, but also led to a false impact warning by a malicious prankster. The first example of the concept of mitigation also emerged at the same time, when, 15 months in advance of the Icarus fly-by, a class of graduate students at Massachusetts Institute of Technology were given a challenging assignment: how to prevent a (simulated) asteroid impact. Project Icarus was the first attempt to assess the scientific and technical means to mitigate a potential impact crisis.

C R   Since its earliest emergence, neo-catastrophism has given rise to a range of initiatives to characterise the impact hazard, including establishment of the Spaceguard Foundation, and collaboration that included observatories across the world aimed at determining and reducing the risk to Earth from bombardment by comets and asteroids by searching for and mapping small Solar System bodies with Earth-crossing orbits. The term **Spaceguard** was coined by the author Arthur C. Clarke, in his novel *Rendezvous with Rama* (1972), referring to an early warning system for asteroid impacts on Earth. The result is that NEOs are now constantly being discovered and reported, and their orbits mapped accurately to determine their closest approach to Earth, up to 100 years into the future.

■   Given your knowledge of asteroid orbit measurements from Chapter 3, why do you think the Spaceguard Survey only considers the next 100 years?

▨   Although astronomical observations are highly precise, there is an uncertainty on any estimate of an asteroid's position, which is magnified when it is extrapolated far into the future. Predictions are therefore only useful for a limited number of orbits. Moreover, the chance of an asteroid orbit being affected by perturbations increases the further into the future that orbit predictions are made.

4.2 NEO risk and risk perception

R   The risk of a large, 10 km diameter NEO collision on Earth is an existential risk; in other words, it is a risk that threatens the very 'existence' of humankind, and differs from other, endurable risks. Human-induced hazards such as BSE/vCJD, world wars, and natural hazards such as tsunami and pandemics can be devastating, even on a global scale, but are not likely to snuff out *Homo sapiens*. The potential threat of a large NEO colliding with Earth constitutes an existential risk because the largest impacts clearly have the potential to jeopardise the continuation of humanity. In fact, until the upsurge of nuclear arsenals in an increasing number of countries in the mid 20th century, species-destroying comet or asteroid impacts had been the only recognised existential risk in human history.

R   The increased recognition of the NEO impact hazard has resulted in research to estimate the risk of NEO collision with Earth. The frequency of NEO collisions with the Earth has been estimated based on crater counts on the Earth and Moon (Chapter 2), and from astronomical observations of the number of asteroids and comets in the Earth's region of the Solar System (Chapter 3). These independent estimates are the basis upon which governments make decisions on the risk of an NEO impact. However, neither estimate is without assumptions and uncertainties. The estimate based on crater counting is subject to some uncertainty due to the difference between the Earth and Moon caused by the effects of Earth's atmosphere and greater gravity. The estimate based on the number of known NEAs is subject to uncertainty because many bodies remain still to be found.

R

In addition to the problems of estimating the direct risk of impact, the secondary environmental effects of cosmic impacts on Earth have not been directly measured, since we have observed only one impact in the technological age, and that was on another Solar System body, when the Shoemaker–Levy 9 comet hit Jupiter. The magnitude, geographical range and duration of these knock-on effects on Earth are based on geophysical and environmental factors which have been incorporated into models to estimate the effects (see Chapter 2). Even less well understood are the potential socio-economic and political consequences on human societies of small or moderate NEO impacts on Earth. The response of governments to the NEO hazard is, therefore, based on the best estimate, or perception, of the risk.

R

Notwithstanding these ambiguities, it is generally agreed that the risk from dying as a result of an impact disaster is dominated by the population of large NEAs. In contrast, long-period comets (of any size) closely approach the Earth at around one-hundredth the frequency with which NEAs approach the Earth. For this reason, a conservative estimate of the fraction of the total impact risk represented by comets is as little as 1% on the basis of observed comet populations. The risk from asteroids, therefore, dominates the risk and most estimates do not consider the risk from comet impact.

R

■ Using Figure 1.4, estimate the probability of death in a once in 1000 year NEO impact event. In terms of extra potential deaths, how much uncertainty does the risk of a comet impact introduce?

The probability of death in a 1 in 1000 year NEO impact event is around 1 in 1 000 000. The comet risk adds an uncertainty of 10 000 deaths in 1 000 000.

C R

Unlike other natural risks such as tsunami and earthquakes, scientists can detect the threatening asteroids via the Spaceguard Survey, perhaps many years before they impact. As more NEOs are found, some argue that the so-called **residual impact hazard** is less than it was, since we actually know where the NEOs are and can determine that their orbits will not intersect the Earth in the next 100 years or more. One view of risk is that it is a measure of the lack of knowledge, so the extension of facts and data inexorably leads to a decrease of risk. Applied to NEOs, this implies that, as the orbits of more asteroids are measured, the risk to Earth is reduced. This inference would be the case even if an unknown asteroid on collision course with Earth were to be detected before impact. The asteroid's certain impact trajectory would replace a residual risk by a definite danger and a certain disaster that could only be averted by way of asteroid destruction or deflection. According to this view of the impact risk, the effect of human observation (the Spaceguard Survey) has been to reduce the risk of an impact. Of the estimated 1090 ± 180 NEAs larger than 1 km, approximately 800 (or 70%) have been discovered at the time of writing (2005).

R

■ If the Spaceguard Survey found all asteroids greater than 1 km diameter, would we be able to forget about the asteroid threat forever?

▓ No, the population of asteroids and their orbits both change with time. First, close encounters and perturbations change an asteroid's orbit; this is why orbits cannot be predicted accurately far into the future. Secondly, the population of NEOs is constantly replenished from the main asteroid belt between Mars and Jupiter as collisions, gravitational perturbations and close approaches project new asteroids into the inner Solar System. Thirdly, asteroids < 1 km diameter are more numerous and still hazardous.

C R

Other scientists argue that the risk does not change as more asteroids are found, just that the risk was always lower than originally estimated. They also point out that the Spaceguard Survey is aimed at detecting asteroids larger than 1 km diameter, and that a Barringer-sized impact (thought to have been caused by a body about 100 m in diameter) and local devastation is still likely to come 'out of the blue'. The debate over how best to assess the NEO impact hazard illustrates the problem that scientists evaluate risk in different and sometimes incompatible ways.

C R

■ What might be the effect upon communicating NEO hazards to decision makers and the general public if experts have substantially divergent conceptions of risk?

▓ Conflicting risk analysis more often than not results in contradictory messages that can range, in extremes, from alarmism to unwarranted reassurance. In this situation, the public and decision makers can lose confidence in messages delivered by any one group of scientists.

4.3 The pitfalls of risk communication

C R

Like other scientific communities, NEO research has seen credible and level-headed risk communication, but also communication that overstated potential danger. The inclination to amplify risk is explicable given that scientists who are seen to be undertaking work of high public interest are likely to have better career prospects. Government funding in the areas of health and safety is strongly influenced by intense private and public lobbying, tempting researchers to promote their specific safety or health risk issues.

However, this is a cynical view of scientists' motivation. Most scientists are motivated by research, discovery and their opportunity to help society rather than a high salary. In many other cases, the dissemination of false, ambiguous or hurried risk alerts is simply done in haste, without thought of the consequences of poor communication, misinterpretation of the message, and/or the result of poor phraseology.

C R E

These societal factors, pressures and temptations have led to a sometimes heated debate within the scientific community over the cost and benefit of risk warnings and false alarms. Some researchers have advocated deliberate scare tactics in order to raise awareness and prompt action over specific, environmental hazards. In a paper published in the journal *Science*, a group of scientists argued that promoting alarmism of natural and environmental hazards is warranted as the end justifies the means. They argue that researchers are often too conservative in issuing warnings due to the uncertainty or improbability of their findings. Since many possible disasters have a very low probability of occurrence at a particular location within a human lifetime, warnings based on tentative data regularly turn out to be groundless if not altogether false. But since the potential benefits of averting disasters are often immense, some people believe that they are probably warranted in continuing to issue what they know are likely to be false alarms.

Conversely, other groups argue that false warnings are quickly derided and promote a lack of trust in the scientists. Professional risk analysts also disapprove of scare tactics. They point out that the detrimental affects of false alarms and the resultant fears are much costlier than generally presumed. David Ropeik of Harvard University's Centre for Risk Analysis, for instance, stresses that the fears themselves are harmful and create a new risk for health, well-being and the stability of societies. As with other low-probability, high-magnitude risks, a significant component of the NEO impact hazard is not the physical risk of dying from an asteroid hit, but how the public perceive this risk.

■ How can public perception of risk from a natural hazard become a hazard in itself?

▨ Warnings of impending catastrophe and memory of catastrophe can unsettle the normal confidence people have in their lives. At a low level it might lead to something as simple as changing a holiday destination. Yet this has had drastic consequences to local economies in Indonesia, Thailand and Sri Lanka following the tsunami disaster of 2004. In extreme cases, such messages might cause panic, demonstrated so graphically by the Orson Welles radio broadcast in 1938 (Chapter 1).

The Roman philosopher Epictetus summed up the same observation two millennia ago when he wrote: 'Men are disturbed not by things, but by the view which they take of them'. There are many consequences of warning messages, particularly if they appear to threaten the status quo.

■ Imagine scientists had predicted precisely the date and time of a major earthquake on the San Andreas Fault. What would be the consequences of a warning of an earthquake predicted to occur months away and one predicted only hours before the earthquake was expected?

▨ An earthquake warning months ahead would make people wary of travelling to California even for business; businesses would falter, and house prices would plummet. People would behave as if their livelihoods were about to be destroyed. If the warning was for an earthquake within hours, people would panic and try to leave, causing grid-lock and many casualties on the roads.

Communicating warning messages to the public and the way they are understood or misunderstood has been a very important part of the research into NEOs. Sometimes, risk overestimation may be the result of incomplete scientific knowledge, but translation of the message into the form of an attractive 'story' for transmission as a 'news item' is another potent way of introducing misconceptions. The process of translation may result in part of a message, say a possible NEO impact, being extracted and transmitted without the attending discussion of uncertainty. Although the journalist may talk directly to a scientist delivering the original message, their views of the actual message can still be different. The scientist may understand that the estimates of asteroid orbits are uncertain and are likely to be altered as more readings are made, and may couch the message in the same conservative language used when talking to other scientists. The journalist may try to extract and distil the important piece of science and formulate an interesting and attractive story which might attract people's attention in competition with the mundane reporting of politics and celebrity gossip. The result is that the message that the scientist thought was being recounted may not be the message received by the public when transmitted.

C R It also remains contentious whether increasingly detailed dissemination of scientific facts significantly affects public risk estimation. Scientists may assume that more communication of statistical or probabilistic information about the NEO impact risk will help the public to see the risk of impact the same way as they do. However, communication of the NEO risk has been accompanied by communication of other risks such as food and health scares, which can leave some people simply adding NEOs to a long list of things they feel they should worry about without placing it in context. In the following sections we will explore the manner in which early communications of NEO impact risk shaped the way in which such messages were treated.

4.4 Asteroid scares

C R Asteroid scares are perhaps the main reason why both media coverage and public concern about the NEO hazard has increased over the years. Comet scares date back to the early 18th century and the reappearance of Halley's Comet, while the era of modern asteroid scares was set in motion when, in 1989, astronomers discovered an asteroid initially designated 1989FC and later named (4581) Asclepius 10 days after it had passed its closest approach to Earth. This scare led to the US Government funding work on NEOs and the beginning of an asteroid search programme in Australia. Soon after, another close approach by an asteroid called 1990 MU led to a question being asked in the European Parliament in Brussels, and consequent media coverage.

C R In one of the earliest predictions of a close approach, in March of 1998, Brian Marsden of the International Astronomical Union's **Minor Planet Center (MPC)** at the Smithsonian Astrophysical Observatory in Harvard, announced that a kilometre-wide asteroid, 1997 XF11, would pass within 19 000 km of Earth in 2028 and that an actual impact was 'not entirely out of the question'.

C ■ Where else have you heard this type of phrase used, and how might it affect public perception of the risk?

■ Politicians use phrases like 'could not be ruled out' when referring to events such as a proposed tax rise or a colleague resigning. Here, the phrase was used to refer to uncertainty in scientific measurements. The listener might hear the same phrase but associate the words with a political context and might believe that the event to which the scientist refers is actually quite likely to happen, but the scientist cannot be seen to say that. This was not the intended message.

The original announcement, which was actually addressed to the NEO search community of scientists, emphasised the uncertainty of the orbit and the need for astronomers to make further observations. Yet, despite the uncertainty and caveats in the original message, the international media picked up the story and turned it into a top news item around the world. The next day, while the front-page headlines of several newspapers proclaimed a possible 'Armageddon' for 2028, Donald Yeomans and Paul Chodas of **JPL/NASA** announced that their analysis of the same data showed that there was no chance of XF11 hitting Earth. Less than 24 hours after the story had broken, the first modern asteroid scare was retracted in an atmosphere of intense public scrutiny. Clearly, the language used to communicate between scientists should not be used to convey a message in the public arena. The announcement had been premature, lacking a formal impact probability calculation and consultation with colleagues.

The global media exposure generated by the false alarm over XF11, together with the release the same year of two blockbuster disaster movies *Deep Impact* and *Armageddon*, raised the public's awareness of the NEO hazard significantly. The media coverage heightened awareness and increased pressure 'to do something', leading the NASA administration to increase its funding for NEO searches (which were already under way, though not well funded) and to the establishment of NASA's NEO office. In the UK, the XF11 affair also triggered, for the first time, debates on NEOs in both the House of Commons and the House of Lords. In response, the UK Government commissioned a rapid report on NEOs from the Parliamentary Office of Science and Technology (POST), which was a scientific document written in relatively jargon-free language describing the state of knowledge and likely risks without making any recommendations. The Government then established the UK Task Force on potentially hazardous NEOs to investigate the risk. The task force published its report in September 2000, describing both the present state of research and work in other countries. It made 12 recommendations. In brief, the report recommended funding for collaborative NEO research across Europe, research into possible mitigation strategies, the appointment of a single department to coordinate policy on NEOs, and the establishment of a UK NEO centre to act as an advisory centre to the government. Finally, and most importantly, the report concluded:

> We recommend that one of the most important functions of a British Centre for near-Earth objects be to provide a public service which would give balanced information in clear, direct and comprehensible language as need might arise. Such a service must respond to very different audiences: on the one hand Parliament, the general public and the media; and on the other the academic, scientific and environmental communities. In all of this, full use should be made of the Internet. As a first step, the Task Force recommends that a feasibility study be established to determine the functions, terms of reference and funding for such a Centre.

> (UK Task Force Report, 2000)

Clearly, the lesson of the XF11 controversy had been learnt, and consideration had to be given to the manner in which warning messages were issued. The problem of how to handle these exceptional asteroids that are, for a fleeting period of time, on a possible collision course with Earth has continued to trouble the NEO research community. There has been an ongoing debate within the community about the dilemma of asteroid scares and how to avoid them. The dramatic increase in NEO discoveries in recent years has led to the discovery of significant numbers of asteroids that might hit the Earth at some point in the distant future. Our knowledge of their future orbits, like those of all NEOs, can never be perfect. An NEO thus has a 'family' of many possible future orbits, all with orbital parameters that are very slightly different, yet still compatible with the observations. If a fraction of these possible orbits results in a collision with the Earth then the object has a non-zero impact probability at some point in the future. The subset of possible orbits that result in a collision are called **virtual impactors**. Such orbits can, in the vast majority of cases, be ruled out by astronomers after further observations reduce the uncertainties in the orbit predictions, thus narrowing down the family of possible future orbits.

C R

As you will see, even since 1998 a number of unsuitably worded and hastily released announcements of possible impact hazards has led to headline-generating false alarms, causing considerable concern and embarrassment within the scientific community. As a result, there have been extensive discussions about the appropriate way temporary impact risks are assessed, handled and communicated both internally and publicly. These asteroid scares have demonstrated that there is a problem in disseminating complex information concerning NEOs whose path is not precisely measured but which might, in the distant future, pass close to Earth.

C R

As you saw in Chapter 3, the orbital arc over which NEOs can be observed from a single point on Earth is relatively short compared to their complete orbit. This means that it may take several nights, or even weeks, of observations to construct an orbit with the level of certainty required to determine whether it might pass close to Earth. In turn, this means that it is often several days or longer after discovery before NEO researchers can determine the likelihood of an Earth-impact trajectory. Only additional observations can establish whether or not the asteroid may be on an actual collision course with Earth. In most cases, it takes only days or weeks of further observations to eliminate the initial, minute risk. Nevertheless, it is vital for the community of professional and amateur astronomers to be notified of new virtual impactors so that crucial follow-up observations can be conducted. This follow-up work improves the precision of the orbit calculations and is part of the way scientists communicate with each other.

C R

The NEO research community is in effect using a 'pooled and peer review' system, in which the information about virtual impactors is routinely pooled and reviewed by peers and colleagues to check the validity of the observations, and then posted on scientific risk websites such as NASA's NEO programme website (Figure 4.2). This communication between astronomers is important, so that those who can confirm the calculations and those observers who can find the objects can start monitoring them as soon as possible.

C

■ What problem might be caused by communication of NEO information via open websites such as NASA's NEO programme impact risk web page shown in Figure 4.2?

Object designation	Year range	Potential impacts	Impact probability (cumulative)	$V_{infinity}$ /km s^{-1}	H (mag)	Estimated diameter /km	Palermo Scale (cumulative)	Palermo Scale (maximum)	Torino Scale (maximum)
2004 VD17	2091–2104	5	1.1×10^{-4}	18.22	18.8	0.580	−1.06	−1.13	1
2004 MN4	2034–2065	9	1.5×10^{-4}	5.86	19.2	0.320	−1.44	−1.75	1
1997 XR2	2101–2101	2	9.7×10^{-5}	7.17	20.8	0.230	−2.44	−2.71	1
1994 WR12	2054–2102	134	1.0×10^{-4}	9.84	22.4	0.110	−2.96	−3.75	0
1979 XB	2056–2101	3	3.3×10^{-7}	24.54	18.5	0.685	−3.07	−3.14	0
2000 SC344	2068–2101	68	1.8×10^{-3}	1.37	24.8	0.040	−3.08	−3.43	0
2000 QS7	2053–2053	2	1.3×10^{-6}	12.32	19.6	0.420	−3.27	−3.46	0
1998 HJ3	2100–2104	3	2.1×10^{-7}	24.09	18.4	0.694	−3.49	−3.69	0
2005 JQ5	2085–2085	1	9.6×10^{-8}	16.55	18.1	0.790	−3.79	−3.79	0

Figure 4.2   List showing the number of close approaches in the given time range, the probability of impact, speed and size for each body, along with both its Torino Scale value and Palermo Scale value, which are explained in the following sections (taken from the NASA NEO programme impact risk web page in 2005). If you check the web page now it will have changed – but you will still be able to find some of the objects. The shading reflects the Torino Scale level.

- The communication between astronomers on such websites is rich in technical jargon and, as such, difficult to understand. The additional problem is that they include estimates of the likelihood of impact which might be clearly associated with indications of uncertainty, but if read by someone without specialist knowledge, might be taken out of context.

The common themes in recent asteroid scares have been hasty publication of essentially correct information about computations that has been inappropriately worded or inaccurately disseminated. This inappropriate communication has triggered a number of scares that have disturbed and distressed the public unnecessarily. In most cases, the crux of the problem was the failure to wait for additional data to arrive, either in the form of new observations or pre-discovery data (looking back in the records of observations for earlier data on what might be the same body (see Activity 3.2)). In numerous cases, the potential hazard was eliminated from the list of threatening asteroids within days of the public announcements of an impact risk.

Once an asteroid is detected, astronomers use measurements of its changing position in the sky to calculate where its orbit will take it over future decades, using techniques you met in Chapter 3. The uncertainty in the orbit prediction is greatest in the first few days and weeks following discovery, and unless it is well tracked there is a danger that it will not be picked up again the next time that its position (in relation to the Earth) is favourable for observations.

Following the XF11 scare, the NEO community hoped that the introduction of an effective risk-communication tool which could be used to convey information of a low-probability hazard would solve the problem of false alarms. Thus, the **Torino Impact Hazard Scale** was launched in 1999 with the stated intention 'to serve as a communication tool for astronomers and the public to assess the seriousness of predictions of close encounters by asteroids and comets during the 21st century'.

R   The Torino Impact Hazard Scale (Figure 4.3) was named after the Italian city in which the scheme was introduced at a meeting in June 1999. It assigns values to the risk posed by asteroids and comets, running from 0 to 10. While an object with a value of 0 or 1 has an extremely low probability of causing damage on Earth, a value of 10 means a certain global catastrophe.

R   The Torino Scale takes into account the object's estimated kinetic energy, as well as the probability that it will collide with Earth on a specific date. In this version of the scale, close approaches, assigned Torino-scale values from 2 to 7, were categorised as ranging from 'events meriting concern' to 'threatening events'. Certain collisions were assigned values of 8, 9 or 10, depending on whether the impact energy is large enough to cause local, regional or global devastation.

Events having no likely consequences	0	The likelihood of a collision is zero, or well below the chance that a random object of the same size will strike the Earth within the next few decades. This designation also applies to any small object that, in the event of a collision, is unlikely to reach the Earth's surface intact.
Events meriting careful monitoring	1	The chance of collision is extremely unlikely, about the same as a random object of the same size striking the Earth within the next few decades.
Events meriting concern	2	A somewhat close, but not unusual encounter. Collision is very unlikely.
	3	A close encounter, with 1% or greater chance of a collision capable of causing localised destruction.
	4	A close encounter, with 1% or greater chance of a collision capable of causing regional devastation.
Threatening events	5	A close encounter, with a significant threat of a collision capable of causing regional devastation.
	6	A close encounter, with a significant threat of a collision capable of causing a global catastrophe.
	7	A close encounter, with an extremely significant threat of a collision capable of causing a global catastrophe.
Certain collisions	8	A collision capable of causing localized destruction. Such events occur somewhere on Earth between once per 50 years and once per 1000 years.
	9	A collision capable of causing regional devastation. Such events occur between once per 1000 years and once per 100 000 years.
	10	A collision capable of causing a global climatic catastrophe. Such events occur once per 100 000 years, or less often.

Figure 4.3   The Torino Impact Hazard Scale, first released in 2000.

C   However, the scale did not achieve universal acceptance even within the NEO community; some researchers considered it too simplistic and prone to misinterpretation. However, by the time the next impact scare hit the global media in 2000 (over a small object by the name of 2000 SG344) the Torino Scale had become the official device of the International Astronomical Union (IAU), against which any probable impact risk was to be measured. In addition, the IAU introduced a 72-hour peer review process that was intended to assess and inspect any impact probability announcements before they were made public. Clearly, anyone transgressing these guidelines risked being ostracised by the community and vilified for issuing a false alarm. However, the first use of the new scale and procedures illustrates just how difficult issuing such a message can be (Box 4.2).

Box 4.2   Premature announcement of possible impact of Asteroid 2000 SG344

C R

On 29 September 2000, a small NEO, designated 2000 SG344, was discovered. The observations indicated that it might be a small asteroid measuring between 30 m and 70 m in diameter, but the unusual nature of its orbit suggested that it was more likely to be a rocket booster from the Apollo era. When, 1 month later, pre-discovery observations of the object were located, it soon became clear to a number of astronomers that this unidentified object might pose a remote but non-zero chance of colliding with Earth. Paul Chodas of the Near-Earth Object Program Office at NASA's Jet Propulsion Laboratory estimated a 1 in 500 probability of the object hitting the Earth on 21 September 2030.

The calculations were verified by a technical review team of the IAU and 72 hours later, this information about a possible Earth impact in 2030 was published by the IAU and NASA. The announcement procedure followed the new IAU guidelines, which demanded that the calculations of a 'significant impact risk' (i.e. NEO close encounters that score 1 or higher on the Torino Scale, see Figure 4.3) should be made public after 72 hours if verified. These guidelines, however, hastened the IAU and NASA into making a premature announcement while astronomers were still searching their databases. Although the statement made clear that additional data would, most likely 'show with certainty that it will miss the Earth entirely', the announcement was published. To make matters worse, some comments made by NASA officials about the potential damage caused by such an impact triggered a global asteroid scare.

The problem with the SG344 announcement and with several other NEO impact scares was that essentially correct computations were announced prematurely, while the data used for the orbital calculations were improving daily. It also became obvious that the Torino Scale had some flaws. In particular, it proved to be an ineffective means of communicating low-probability risks of asteroid impact with Earth. The most important flaw seemed to be that at level 1, the scale could not discriminate between risk of imminent impacts about which people should worry and impacts predicted far in the future which are likely to be disproved with further data. In fact, it would be possible for objects to reach Torino level 6 or 7 (presumably with the associated worry to the public) before plummeting to zero as extra data allow the object's orbit to be calculated more precisely.

After much discussion in the NEO community, an attempt was made to remedy the pitfalls of the Torino Scale, and the **Palermo Technical Impact Hazard Scale** was launched in 2001. It was mainly designed for professional usage, but also to address some of the deficiencies of the Torino Scale.

C

The Palermo Technical Impact Hazard Scale was developed to enable NEO specialists to categorise and prioritise potential impact risks spanning a wide range of impact dates, energies and probabilities. The Palermo Scale value is calculated from the probability of impact, divided by the time till the impact and

C R

the annual background impact frequency. In other words, it is the ratio of the probability of impact (for a particular close encounter) compared to the background likelihood of an impact of the same or greater energy happening before that date. The Palermo Scale value allows scientists to judge the seriousness of the threat since it includes a measure of the likelihood of the event actually happening. Predicted impacts far in the future or impacts by smaller bodies thus score lower on the Palermo Scale than imminent impacts or larger asteroid bodies.

C R The Palermo Scale is a logarithmic scale. Like the Richter scale for earthquakes, each value on the scale is 10 times the previous. So, for example, a level 5 earthquake is 10 times as powerful as a level 4 earthquake. Palermo Scale values of less than −2 reflect events for which there are no likely consequences, while values between −2 and 0 indicate situations that 'merit careful monitoring' but no special attention. No mention is made of hazard in the Palermo Scale values in this range. Potential impacts with positive Palermo Scale values indicate situations that merit additional attention and some level of concern.

C More recently the IAU have revised the wording of the Torino Scale using clearer and less-technical language in an attempt to make the transmission of message clearer (Figure 4.4)

C ■ What are the important differences in the explanation of the level of concern warranted for level 0 and level 1 NEOs in the two versions of the Torino Scale?

▨ The wording in the new scale uses language without scientific caveats, and makes clear who should be concerned at each level. For example, the wording 'events having no likely consequences' in the earlier scale (Figure 4.3) was replaced by 'no hazard' in the later version (Figure 4.4) and 'events meriting careful monitoring' (Figure 4.3) became 'normal' in the later version (Figure 4.4). Clearly, events which the scientific community consider 'normal' are not newsworthy.

At the time of writing, the asteroid predicted to have the closest approach to Earth, (99942) Apophis, will pass Earth at one-tenth of the distance between the Earth and the Moon, around 24 000 to 40 000 kilometres from Earth in April 2029. The object will probably be large and close enough to be seen with the naked eye.

C R ■ From the statement above, what level does (99942) Apophis have on the Torino Scale and should we be concerned about it?

▨ The asteroid is going to pass very close to Earth but the distances are clearly well constrained, which indicates that sufficient observations have been made to determine that it will not impact on this close approach. As such, it has a Torino Scale level 1, in the normal or green zone.

The determination of the orbit of (99942) Apophis illustrates a final problem with NEOs. The asteroid will pass sufficiently close to Earth that the Earth's gravity will alter its orbit, and future close passes are thus less predictable. It may move further away, or it may mean that future impacts are more likely.

No hazard	0	The likelihood of collision is zero, or is so low as to be effectively zero. Also applies to small objects such as meteors and fireballs that burn up in the atmosphere as well as infrequent meteorite falls that rarely cause damage.
Normal	1	A routine discovery in which a pass near the Earth is predicted that poses no unusual level of danger. Current calculations show the chance of collision is extremely unlikely with no cause for public attention or public concern. New telescopic observations very likely will lead to re-assignment to Level 0.
Meriting attention by astronomers	2	A discovery, which may become routine with expanded searches, of an object making a somewhat close but not highly unusual pass near the Earth. While meriting attention by astronomers, there is no cause for public attention or public concern as an actual collision is very unlikely. New telescopic observations very likely will lead to re-assignment to Level 0.
	3	A close encounter, meriting attention by astronomers. Current calculations give a 1% or greater chance of collision capable of localized destruction. Most likely, new telescopic observations will lead to re-assignment to Level 0. Attention by the public and by public officials is merited if the encounter is less than a decade away.
	4	A close encounter, meriting attention by astronomers. Current calculations give a 1% or greater chance of collision capable of regional devastation. Most likely, new telescopic observations will lead to re-assignment to Level 0. Attention by the public and by public officials is merited if the encounter is less than a decade away.
Threatening	5	A close encounter posing a serious, but still uncertain threat of regional devastation. Critical attention by astronomers is needed to determine conclusively whether or not a collision will occur. If the encounter is less than a decade away, governmental contingency planning may be warranted.
	6	A close encounter by a large object posing a serious, but still uncertain threat of a global catastrophe. Critical attention by astronomers is needed to determine conclusively whether or not a collision will occur. If the encounter is less than three decades away, governmental contingency may be warranted.
	7	A very close encounter by a large object, which if occurring this century, poses an unprecedented but still uncertain threat of a global catastrophe. For such a threat in this century, international contingency planning is warranted, especially to determine urgently and conclusively whether or not a collision will occur.
Certain collisions	8	A collision is certain, capable of causing localized destruction for an impact over land or possibly a tsunami if close offshore. Such events occur on average between once per 50 years and once per several 1000 years.
	9	A collision is certain, capable of causing unprecedented regional devastation for a land impact or the threat of a major tsunami for an ocean impact. Such events occur on average between once per 10 000 years and once per 100 000 years.
	10	A collision is certain, capable of causing a global climatic catastrophe that may threaten the future of civilization as we know it, whether impacting land or ocean. Such events occur on average once per 100 000 years, or less often.

Figure 4.4   The revised Torino Scale (2004).

4.5 Impact disaster management: what if?

CRE

Since 1985, technological and computational advances have significantly improved the rate of detection of potentially hazardous NEOs. The improvements in technology mean that scientists have been able to quantify a fundamental threat to humanity and persuade decision makers that the threat is real. The same developments have also meant that news of NEO discoveries is transmitted globally very quickly. This progress can be measured against an intensification of NEO discoveries, improved telescope technology and the advance of computer technologies for image analysis. Equally important has been the expansion of advanced computational systems at the IAU's Minor Planet Centre (MPC) and the establishment of impact probability programmes at Pisa University and NASA's NEO Program Office. These developments have greatly augmented predictive capabilities and thus expanded impact warning times considerably.

R

It is certain that, one day, astronomers will detect an NEO on a collision course with Earth; indeed, some 40% of all Earth-crossing asteroids will collide with Earth eventually. This could happen tomorrow or it could occur one hundred or a million years from now. It could be a small asteroid or medium-sized comet, or it could be a larger object. Happily, the chances are extremely small that this will happen soon. None the less, such an event will transpire one day. And when it happens, it will be unprecedented. Since we have no experience with such an emergency, the first predicted impact disaster crisis will confront us with considerable social, technological and managerial challenges.

R

The NEO impact hazard from the largest bodies is beyond what we can plan for. A once in 100 million year global catastrophe such as the K/T boundary event is also such an unlikely event that, despite its apocalyptic horror, all that science and policy makers can do is work on finding such objects as quickly as possible and initiate space-based mitigation strategies. In Section 4.7, we will discuss the possible deflection or destruction of an NEO predicted to impact many years after its detection. However, the most likely NEO impact that society will face is not a once in 100 million year event but a smaller Tunguska or Barringer Crater-type event. Although an NEO impact is outside our experience and would be devastating to the local environment, it is likely to be manifested as a series of the more common natural hazards such as fire, flood and perhaps famine.

R

■ What is the most likely natural hazard the world will face as the result of an NEO impact?

▨ 70% of the world's surface is covered by ocean and thus the most likely NEO impact hazard is actually a tsunami in an area unused to earthquakes.

C R

Disaster warning systems have become essential social mechanisms in the forecast, detection and mitigation of natural disasters. Societies exposed to natural hazards are increasingly relying on the effectiveness of such warning systems. However, the human disaster following the tsunami in the Indian Ocean on 26 December 2004 illustrates that, even with some alarm capability, natural disasters still occur without warning.

C R

Given the rudimentary structure of the current NEO impact warning system, the event most likely to occur during our lifetimes is the impact of a small undetected asteroid. The most likely event is the explosion of a Tunguska-sized NEO in the atmosphere which would be detected by earthquake warning centres (including the ITIC) around the world. Of the 29 documented smallish impacts that occurred in the decade between 1990 and 2000, more than 90% happened in or over uninhabited parts of the world. As long as NEO search programmes are primarily terrestrial rather than space-based, almost all of the small, Tunguska-type impacts will likely come 'out of the blue', that is without prior detection, and it will be impossible to issue any public warning. Nevertheless, it would be prudent not to underestimate the social and psychological disturbances a sudden, unpredicted asteroid impact may set off.

If we were to witness a 20–100 megatonne NEO impact such as the Barringer Crater event, the view of many people about their sense of safety would change dramatically. Individuals would become more anxious about the risk of future impacts given that increased media coverage may intensify stress levels and anxiety about the risk. Many people distressed by a minor impact disaster would start to see the world as threatened by cosmic danger. Some people might experience problems in dealing with even a small impact due to its random and 'terrorising' nature. It would also stir up anxieties not least because the impact is likely to be the subject of intense and lengthy media coverage. Finally, some people will feel very angry, and scared, and will blame their governments, space agencies and astronomers for failing to protect them from cosmic disaster.

R

Unlike most other natural hazard warnings that are usually delivered to just the people at risk from a local or regional disaster, an initial NEO impact warning will need to be delivered to a global audience. In order to minimise public anxiety in response to an impact warning, it will be imperative to calculate and announce (as early as possible) impact location probabilities for certain areas of the globe. Even if the impact probability for a small or medium-sized NEO reaches 100%, the personal risk probability (i.e. the chance of being physically affected as a result of the impact and its secondary destructive effects) would remain close to 1 in a million and the risk would come in the form of conventional natural risks such as tsunami (Chapter 2). Naturally, the bigger the size of the impactor, the higher the personal risk probability will be – until the NEO reaches the 1–2 km threshold that would more or less affect everyone.

C R

- ■ If one day, hopefully far in the future, astronomers confirm an impact probability has reached 100%, what could be done in order to reduce fear?

C R

- ■ The most important task would be to narrow down the impact location and to estimate the probable secondary impact effects likely to result from an impact in the region.

The last 2 to 3 days before impact would be spent narrowing down the region where the impact would probably occur. Although it sounds easy, this is a difficult calculation because the Earth is both travelling along its orbit and also spinning on its axis. Although the Earth is travelling at around 29.8 km s^{-1} along its orbit, the final impact site depends equally upon the Earth's rotation.

- ■ Given that the average radius of the Earth is 6371 km, and it rotates once every 24 hours, what would be the effect on the point of impact of a 1 hour difference in the asteroid impact time at the Equator? (The circumference of the Earth is given by the formula $2\pi r$.)

- ■ Circumference of the Earth = $2 \times \pi \times 6371$ km = 40 030 km. A 1 hour difference in the arrival time might mean as much as 1668 km for the site of impact (calculated by dividing 40 030 km by 24). Clearly, this might be the difference between ocean, uninhabited land or densely occupied city.

Given the precision to which astronomical observations can be made, it is likely that, were an asteroid to be identified on an intercept path with Earth, the impact point would be narrowed to an area of 1000 km diameter some 72–48 hours before

C R

impact, and that the area would gradually shrink as more observations became available. Consequently, the last 2 or 3 days would have to be used to evacuate population centres, should there be any close to the impact area. Note, however, that the impact location is much more likely to be unpopulated or, even more likely, ocean. It would only be possible to achieve such a task if it were coordinated through government, and perhaps military agencies. Whilst the announcement of the impact location would increase stress and anxiety for people in the vicinity of the predicted impact, it would provide vital warning time to evacuate areas should this be necessary. It would certainly provide reassurances to all those around the world that would not be affected. Nevertheless, the final 48 hours would be crucial to reduce the potential loss of life in such a disaster.

C R

The idea of calculating the impact probability for certain areas of the globe is important because it introduces a new aspect to the question of impact risk. It would also help to reassure an apprehensive population around the globe. In the event of a confirmed impact of a 50–200 m object, the probability of any given city being affected by the impact will be only around 1 in a million (see Chapter 1). This knowledge would have to be part of the main message conveyed to the international public. Only a relatively small geographical area of the globe will be strongly affected (though the reach of a tsunami might be greater as we saw in Chapter 1). Such an announcement might induce economic stresses, including a huge slump in business activity close to the impact, house price falls or changes in holiday destinations – all these effects could have severe long-term implications. Perhaps the most severe problems, however, will result from panic and attempts to evacuate areas believed to be at risk, causing refugee problems in adjacent areas.

C

During the impact mitigation phase, the most important policy group would not be the IAU, but possibly a United Nations NEO Panel, with its geographical involvement and disaster-management expertise complementing that of the astronomers and military experts. If such a scenario should occur tomorrow, we would not be well prepared – neither regarding the way we would handle the communication nor with regard to international management structures that simply have not yet been established.

C R

The big question is: how high does the risk level have to go, and using which measure of risk, before governments take an interest? In assessing that question, one needs to be watching how the probability of impact changes with time, particularly in comparison with the time remaining until the assumed impact. Although the Torino Scale levels 8, 9, and 10 are designed to communicate highly dangerous situations, they are static and it is likely that communications would be dominated by estimates of impact time, location and likely size of the area of damage.

4.6 The response to the NEO hazard

R

As you saw in Chapter 3, there has been an international response from scientists (though dominantly in the USA) and governments to the NEO impact hazard, particularly because this threat does not respect national boundaries. The first response has been the establishment of the Spaceguard Survey (taking its name from the title of the Spaceguard Report (Morrison, 1992)), much of which is NASA funded, but represents an international effort involving telescopes around the world.

The NASA Spaceguard goal is to find and measure 90% of the short-period Earth-approaching asteroids by 2008, examine their orbits and determine if any will collide with the Earth during the next century. The Spaceguard Survey passed its halfway mark in mid-2000. This systematic search strategy should enable scientists to have sufficient warning to start work to avert a potential impact and protect the world from a global hazard.

As of November 2005, there were 3681 known NEAs, and 812 of these are large NEAs. In this context, 'large' is defined as an asteroid having an absolute magnitude of 18.0 or brighter, which roughly corresponds to diameters of 1 km or larger as you saw in Chapter 3. In contrast, the number of known NECs currently number only 57, and are increasing at the rate of about two per year. It is believed that about 75% of large NEAs have been detected so far, assuming that the estimated total is indeed in the region of 1090.

While the overall discovery rate for NEAs has grown steadily since 1995, there has been a noticeable slow-down in recent years in the discovery rate of NEAs larger than 1 km. It is generally assumed that this is a reflection of the fact that we have already discovered a large fraction of this population group.

Having reached the 75% milestone, the Spaceguard Survey has (at the time of writing, November 2005) three more years to increase the number of known large NEAs from just over 800 to the 90% goal (i.e. around 980). To meet this goal, the current discovery rate of about 50 per year will need to be maintained by improvements in the system to compensate for a shrinking pool of undiscovered objects. In this way, the Spaceguard Survey is progressing toward meeting its 90% goal sometime between 2008 and 2010. The number of NEAs known in the years 1980 to 2005 is shown in Figure 4.5. You can see the dramatic increase in the rate of detection in the late 1990s, and the slower rate of increase in the number of large NEAs since 2002.

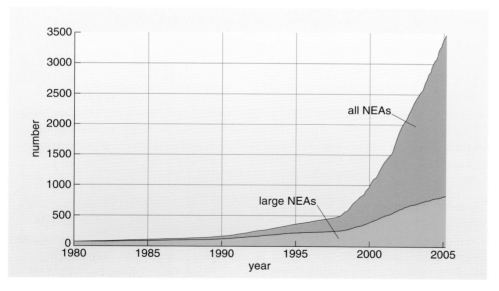

Figure 4.5   Plot of cumulative total of known NEAs (January 1980 to March 2005). Shown in blue are the data for all NEAs, while those for 'large' (magnitude 18.0 or brighter) NEAs are shown in red.

Much of the Spaceguard Survey has been undertaken by groups such as the Lincoln Near-Earth Asteroid Research (LINEAR) group. In cooperation with the US Air Force, the Massachusetts Institute of Technology's Lincoln laboratory has been operating telescopes in Socorro, New Mexico, originally designed to observe Earth-orbiting spacecraft. The LINEAR group have detected over 200 000 asteroids (most of which lie in the asteroid Main Belt).

Much of the early work has been undertaken by small telescopes, but much bigger survey telescopes such as the Panoramic Survey Telescope and Rapid Response System (Pan-STARRS) in Hawaii and the Discovery Channel Telescope (DCT) at Lowell Observatory will revolutionise future NEO search strategies.

The first of four large telescopes in Pan-STARRS will operate on Haleakala, Maui, Hawaii. When the full telescope array is completed in 2007, it is expected to detect about 100 000 asteroids per month. The system will enable astronomers to detect objects as small as 100 metres in diameter and 100 times fainter than those observed by other telescopes.

The 4-metre DCT – designed for the Lowell Observatory in Flagstaff, Arizona, and expected to be completed in 2008 – will be amongst the most sophisticated ground-based telescopes of its size. Once complete, the DCT will make it possible to identify the same number of potentially hazardous NEAs as detected by the Spaceguard Survey thus far in just 30 days.

R

The Spaceguard project has already greatly improved knowledge of the NEO hazard. Ten years ago, it was thought that there were some 2000 unknown large NEAs that had the potential to cause a global catastrophe. Since then, with improved measurements and observations, the estimated number of large NEAs has been reduced by almost half, to 1090 ± 180. In addition, astronomers have discovered more than 50% of the large Main Belt asteroids that are theoretically capable of causing global devastation.

4.7 Strategies for mitigation

C E

The UK Government Task Force Report recommendations included not only an effort to search for NEOs, but also the development of techniques that could 'do something about it'. If an NEO more than a few metres across is detected on an impact course years before impact, the opportunity to prevent its collision with Earth is likely to be grasped by humankind. Asteroids less than around 50 m in diameter are still likely to hit 'out of the blue', most likely in the ocean or an uninhabited part of the Earth, with few directly related fatalities.

R

There are several ways in which technology could be used to mitigate the threat from an NEO on a predicted collision course with the Earth. For the smallest-sized objects, it may be best (in other words, most cost-effective) to mitigate the threat by preparations on the ground, as you saw earlier in this chapter, for example by evacuating the predicted area of impact destruction. For larger, more potentially destructive objects, a space-based solution is a more attractive option, albeit an ambitious one. With sufficient warning time, funding and technology, an NEO could be either destroyed or deflected, so that it no longer poses a threat.

The Spaceguard effort is likely to mean that NEO warning times will be many years, even decades or centuries, as smaller and smaller NEOs are discovered and tracked with greater accuracy and precision. With long-period comets, however, warning times are unlikely to be more than a couple of years at best, given the difficulty of discovering potential impactors in the cold, far reaches of the Solar System and predicting their path through the inner Solar System.

Many approaches to space-based mitigation have been put forward and studied to varying degrees. They range from practical solutions within the capability of technology available today, to much more speculative concepts that are more within the realms of science fiction. Such mitigation strategies aim for either destruction or deflection of the NEO, and are either quick or slow in the way they work. Table 4.1 gives examples of these four possibilities.

Table 4.1 Some quick and slow approaches to destroying or deflecting a threatening NEO.

	Destruction	**Deflection**
Quick	Nuclear detonation inside the NEO to blow it apart into many dispersed, small pieces	Nuclear detonation a short distance from the NEO to blast material from the surface and push it in the opposite direction
		Hitting the NEO with a large mass travelling at high speed to change its orbit slightly
Slow	Mining the NEO and removing the material to elsewhere	Altering the NEO's surface to change the effect of non-gravitational forces (e.g. radiation pressure) on its future orbit
		Attaching a rocket propulsion system to the NEO's surface to propel it onto an orbit that misses the Earth
		Using a large mirror to concentrate sunlight onto the NEO's surface to vaporise material from the surface and gently push the NEO in the opposite direction

The mitigation solution chosen would depend on many factors, including the warning time, the size of the object, the technological readiness and reliability of the approach. There are also risks inherent in some of the approaches. For example, in the case of destruction by nuclear detonation it may be possible that large fragments survive on a collision course for Earth and still cause destruction. Another risk is that an NEO is fragmented only for much of it to come back together again due to the mutual gravitational attraction of the pieces.

Deflection techniques would work either by changing the direction of an NEO's orbital path so that it misses the Earth, or by speeding up or slowing down an NEO along the direction of its orbit to change the semi-major axis and thus the orbital period.

■ How would this second method avoid a collision with the Earth?

▨ Since the NEO's orbital period would change, it would take a slightly longer or shorter time to arrive at the Earth's orbit. The result would be that it would cross the Earth's orbit, but the Earth would be somewhere else on its orbit at the time and so the NEO would miss.

Attempts at deflections can be fast, like a spacecraft impact or nuclear detonation at a short distance from the NEO, or slow, like attaching a rocket propulsion system to the surface to propel the NEO into a different orbit over a long period of time. Although both fast and slow deflection options sound feasible, you should remember that the NEO has an enormous amount of kinetic energy. As you saw in Chapter 2, the collision of an NEO with Earth results in the sudden release of this kinetic energy that, for a 1 km diameter NEO, might be around 3.2×10^{20} J and exceed the combined energy that would be released by all nuclear weapons on Earth. Although it would take less energy to shift an NEO a few km 'out of orbit' if it was discovered a few years before impact, moving a mass of around 1.6×10^{12} kg would require either an explosion of many nuclear weapons in the hope that the body did not fragment or a sustained 'push' that is beyond current rocket motors. However, orbit changes that amount to as little as 1 mm s^{-1} can result in significant change if they happen sufficiently far in advance.

■ What change in distance (in km) would result from travelling at 1 mm s^{-1} faster or slower for 1 year? (Recall that there are 3.2×10^7 s in 1 year.)

▨ Distance is speed multiplied by time, so the distance travelled is 1 mm s^{-1} × 3.2×10^7 s, which is 3.2×10^7 mm. There are 10^6 mm in a kilometre so this distance is equal to 3.2×10^7 mm/10^6 mm km^{-1} = 32 km.

Some effort is now being extended to determine the best methods to deflect NEOs, including the best points within the orbit to attempt deflection, and the relative advantages of fast and slow deflection. While there is currently no 'ready and waiting' capability to destroy or deflect an NEO, there are, clearly, some technological solutions within humankind's grasp that could be brought to bear if an NEO were found to be on a collision course with Earth.

R   Some have argued that humankind should assemble an arsenal of nuclear weapons ready to launch against an NEO, but others disagree and argue that this would pose a greater risk than the NEO threat itself. Much depends on what the NEO surveys find; that is to say, whether or not they reveal any objects heading for Earth within the next century or so.

A spectacular example of how an impact deflection technique might work occurred on 4 July 2005 when the Deep Impact robotic space mission encountered the nucleus of comet Tempel 1, with the aim of studying a range of physical properties of a comet nucleus. The spacecraft separated into two parts shortly before encountering the comet nucleus at 10.2 km s^{-1}. One part of the craft performed remote observations as it flew by, while the other, a 370 kg impactor, hit the surface of the comet nucleus. Although the impact was not large enough to cause a significant change in the comet's orbit, it did demonstrate the targeting technology required and produced a bright impact flash and a plume of dust and gas from the crater (Figure 4.6).

Figure 4.6   This image of comet Tempel 1 was taken 67 seconds after it obliterated Deep Impact's impactor spacecraft. The image was taken by the camera on the mission's fly-by craft. Scattered light from the collision created the bright flash seen in the image. The comet nucleus is approximately 7 km across.

Activity 4.1 (Part 2)

Allow 15 minutes

Go back over the chapter and locate the places where you placed a D in the margin and compare your choices with those suggested in the 'Comments on activities' section at the back of this book. Short explanations of our choice are also provided. How do these explanations compare with your own notes?

Summary of Chapter 4

1   The discovery of asteroids and comets changed human perception of the Solar System from a benign environment to one that might threaten and possibly bring catastrophe upon the human race from the sky.

2   The subject of NEOs has been brought to public attention through a series of asteroid close approach scares, the Shoemaker–Levy 9 impact on Jupiter in 1994 and a number of books and films.

3   Early asteroid scares were the result of the lack of communication expertise, but served to heighten public awareness. They also tended to reduce public confidence in the work to find NEOs and understand the hazard.

4   Government response in funding the Spaceguard Survey to find NEOs created the need to communicate levels of risk to the public in a reasoned and coherent manner. The Torino Scale and Palermo Scales were created for the purpose of communicating the risk of impact. While the Torino Scale was created in order to communicate risk clearly to the public, the Palermo Scale is an estimate of the impact risk against the background risk, used mainly for communication within the NEO community. An early version of the Torino Scale wording had some failings and has evolved to improve communication.

5   If an impact were ever to be predicted, it is likely that only a small area of the Earth would be affected, but the public perception of the hazard might be almost as dangerous as the actual impact. Economic dangers, including things as simple as house prices and changing holiday destinations, can have severe economic implications.

6   The collaborative effort to find and track NEOs is succeeding in finding the estimated 1090 ± 180 NEAs larger than 1 km, but the next step will be to find yet smaller NEAs.

7   Strategies for mitigation of the NEO hazard can involve destruction, deflection or mitigation on Earth by evacuation.

8   There are technologically conceivable mitigation strategies that involve either destruction or deflection of the threatening NEO. Some solutions would act rapidly, others more slowly.

Questions for Chapter 4

Question 4.1

Briefly describe two examples of misunderstanding resulting from the use of scientific language to communicate the risk of NEO impact on Earth to the public.

Question 4.2

Comet Tempel 1 was first observed in 1867 by Ernest Tempel, whilst he was working in Marseille. After being lost for many years, the comet was rediscovered in the 1960s by the American astronomer Brian Marsden. Tempel 1 is now best known for the Deep Impact mission described in Section 4.7. The orbital parameters based on astronomical measurements since the discovery of Tempel 1 are shown in Table 4.2. Use these data to answer the following questions concerning Tempel 1.

Table 4.2   Orbital parameters of Comet Tempel 1 based on astronomical measurements since its discovery.

	P/y	a/AU	q/AU	Q/AU	e
1867 May	5.65	3.17	1.56	4.78	0.51
1873 May	5.98	3.29	1.77	4.81	0.46
1879 May	5.98	3.29	1.77	4.81	0.46
1885 Sept	6.50	3.48	2.07	4.89	0.40
1937 Dec	6.50	3.48	2.07	4.89	0.40
1944 May	5.84	3.24	1.69	4.79	0.48
1950 Mar	5.84	3.24	1.69	4.79	0.48
1955 Dec	5.55	3.13	1.53	4.73	0.51
1967 Jan	5.51	3.12	1.50	4.73	0.52
1972 July	5.50	3.11	1.50	4.72	0.52
1978 Jan	5.50	3.11	1.50	4.72	0.52
1983 July	5.49	3.11	1.49	4.73	0.52
1989 Jan	5.50	3.11	1.50	4.72	0.52
1994 July	5.50	3.11	1.49	4.73	0.52
2000 Jan	5.51	3.12	1.50	4.73	0.52
2005 July	5.51	3.12	1.51	4.72	0.52

(a) Is comet Tempel 1 an NEO?

(b) What simple conclusions can you draw concerning the history of the orbit of Tempel 1 from the astronomical observations in Table 4.2? (*Hint*: pay particular attention to the observations above and below the gaps in the table.)

(c) Following your answer to (b), and using Figure 3.7, speculate as to what might have happened to Tempel 1 during the periods May 1867 to May 1873, December 1937 to May 1944, and March 1950 to December 1955.

Question 4.3

(a) In Chapter 2, an estimate of the rate of asteroid collisions with Earth at around 250 craters every 100 million years was derived using the number of large craters on stable areas of the Earth's crust. Using Figure 2.17, estimate the number of 20 km craters on the Earth every 100 million years based on the lunar mare.

(b) Briefly outline the reasons why the two numbers should coincide but are actually slightly different.

(c) Telescope observations of NEOs provide an estimate of average time between impacts of 1 km diameter asteroids of 0.6 million years. Thus in 100 million years, we would predict around 167 impacts. Given that asteroids of 1 km diameter are likely to cause 20–30 km craters on Earth, comment on the difference between the collision rate derived from NEO observations and those derived from crater counting.

Learning Outcomes for Topic 2

S250's Learning Outcomes are listed in the *Course Guide* under three categories: Knowledge and understanding (Kn1–Kn6), Cognitive skills (C1–C5) and Key skills (Ky1–Ky6). Here we outline how these overall Learning Outcomes are treated in the context of NEOs and the impact hazard.

The knowledge and understanding outcomes for NEOs relate mainly to the astronomical observations of orbits of asteroids and comets, and the effects of past asteroid and comet collisions with Earth (Kn1 and Kn2). You are assumed to have a basic understanding of the Solar System from previous studies. Kn3 relates to the crucial differences in communication between groups of scientists, and between scientists and the public. Estimates of the rate at which objects of different sizes collide with Earth, based on telescope observations of asteroids and crater counting on the Moon and Earth form an important aspect of the science, but the public perception of risk is an equally important aspect of this topic (Kn4). Comparison of these different estimates of risk, and the ways in which risk has been communicated to the public, will develop your ability to assess science communication and the ways risk is expressed (Kn4). The problem of what to do if scientists discover an NEO on a collision course with Earth will develop your understanding of the ethics of disaster management (Kn5). The hazard of NEO impact is global, and has led to a global response from the public and decision makers alike (Kn6).

Having studied NEOs and the impact hazard, you should be able to apply your knowledge and understanding to future developments in the search for asteroids and comets, and future announcements of asteroid close-approach and impact threat, given information about the orbits and sizes of the bodies (C1). In particular, you should be able to recognise whether or not newly discovered bodies actually pose a significant threat to Earth (C2), and what sizes of body may have caused impacts in the past. You should be able to make defensible judgements, based on the evidence, of the competing views of the likely risk of an NEO collision with Earth, and the factors that may affect the orbits of small bodies (C3, C5). You should also be able to recognise the limits of information that can be gleaned from astronomical observations of Solar System bodies arising from the limited accuracy of orbit predictions and the lack of data on composition and density (C4). In addition, you should be able to recognise the limits of using data from studies of ancient craters on the Moon in explaining impacts on the Earth, resulting from its different gravity and the presence of an atmosphere (C4).

Studying NEOs and the impact hazard provides opportunities to develop key skills, including receiving and responding to information from the course material and other sources such as the DVD-ROM and websites (Ky1). There are exercises designed to enable you to understand asteroid and comet orbits and impacts on Earth that will develop your ability to interpret and present qualitative and quantitative data and improve your numeracy skills (Ky2, Ky3). You should also have opportunities to communicate with others in writing or by other means (Ky4). You should aim to use every opportunity to improve your own understanding by working with others (Ky5) and also to improve the effectiveness of your own learning and performance (Ky6).

Answers to questions

Question 1.1

The size of the impact and explosion are related to the kinetic energy of the body, which is transformed into light, sound and heat upon impact. The difference in the hazard is thus governed by the difference in kinetic energy of the two bodies.

The equation for kinetic energy is: $E_k = \frac{1}{2}mv^2$

Comets may be travelling at speeds as high as 75 km s^{-1}, whereas the speed of asteroids range from 10 km s^{-1} to 30 km s^{-1}.

Thus using the kinetic energy (Equation 1.1) for the two bodies yields:

$$E1_k = \frac{1}{2} \times m \times (75\,000 \text{ m s}^{-1})^2 \text{ (for the comet)}$$

and

$$E2_k = \frac{1}{2} \times m \times (30\,000 \text{ m s}^{-1})^2 \text{ (for the asteroid)}$$

If the masses are the same, the difference in kinetic energy is proportional to the differences in speed, which is squared in the equation. Dividing the two equations yields

$$\frac{E1_k}{E2_k} = \frac{5.6 \times 10^9}{9 \times 10^8} = 6.2$$

Even though they have the same mass, the comet has over 6 times the kinetic energy and thus poses a far greater threat to Earth since the size of the explosion and resulting crater depend upon the kinetic energy of the impacting body.

Question 1.2

Many naturally occurring low-probability, but potentially catastrophic, events are extremely difficult to predict, and making predictions that turn out to be false very quickly erode public confidence. An example might be issuing a warning that a volcano is about to erupt. If the prediction proves to be a false warning, the public begin ignoring warnings, accusing scientists of 'crying wolf', or perhaps of trying to obtain funding for research into the threat. Conversely, neglecting to warn of an event that subsequently proves important can attract accusations of a 'cover-up' or incompetence.

Question 2.1

Since the radius of a circle is half the diameter, the area of a circle of 25 km diameter $= \pi r^2 = \pi \times (12.5 \text{ km})^2$, which is 491 km^2. Dividing the total surface area of the Earth by the area affected (5.101×10^8 km^2/491 km^2) indicates that the area constitutes just 1 part in 1 038 900 of the Earth's total surface area (roughly one in a million). In other words, in the event of a Barringer-type collision, the probability of a particular city being devastated is one in a million. In fact, it might be argued that a partial hit would be devastating, but even allowing for an extra 12.5 km around the city, yields a probability of 1 in 259 800 for a zone of minor damage.

Question 2.2

(a) Three-fifths of the Earth's surface is covered by ocean, so the ocean is most likely to be hit by a meteorite.

(b) (i) The most likely hazard resulting from an NEO impact is a tsunami (mega wave) caused by an impact in the ocean. The tsunami caused by the 26 December 2004 earthquake (Chapter 1) demonstrated that tsunami carry immense amounts of energy, travel thousands of kilometres across the ocean surface, and can cause widespread devastation to low-lying, often highly populated, areas of land. The oceans not normally associated with earthquake-generated tsunami, such as the Atlantic Ocean, could also be hit and thus the hazard is greater because they do not have a tsunami warning system. (ii) The main hazards from an impact on land are either the effects of the explosion in the local area or, alternatively, at greater distances, crop failure and climate change brought about by dust in the stratosphere.

Question 2.3

(a) Yes, the two estimates are within reasonable bounds, even though Figure 2.17 shows that the Earth is hit by far more NEOs than the Moon. This is because the difference is similar to the difference in their surface areas, in other words the Earth is hit by around 13 times as many impacts as the Moon for the equivalent diameter NEO. The estimates are based upon crater counting on the lunar mare and old areas of the Earth's continental crust, two very different environments of very different ages, so we might expect some differences. In addition, we might expect that the Earth's greater gravity and atmosphere would affect the size and number of craters formed. Thus, the near coincidence of the terrestrial line and the dashed lunar mare extrapolation is confirmation of the similar impact histories of the Earth and the Moon. The main difference we see is the reduction of smaller craters on Earth that might be the result of break-up in the Earth's atmosphere or erosion of the Earth's surface.

(b) The cratering rates for the Earth and Moon are similar because the two have been together for over 4500 million years and have thus seen the same rate of asteroids and comets in the inner Solar System.

The cratering rate derived for the moon is based on craters which have formed on the lunar mare over the last 3600 million years. The cratering rate for the Earth is based on craters formed on continents over the last 100 million years. The fact that the two numbers coincide implies a similar cratering rate for the last 3600 million years both on the Earth and the Moon.

There are two possible reasons why the Earth appears to have fewer small craters per unit area compared with the Moon. First, craters on Earth smaller than 1 km across may be as little as 100 m deep and are quickly filled by sediments or, more likely, rapidly eroded. An alternative hypothesis is that many smaller asteroids are actually not solid objects; rather they are rubble piles and break up as they pass through the Earth's atmosphere.

Question 2.4

No, the estimate of the rate of crater formation on Earth is an average over millions of years. Asteroids do not arrive at regular intervals; they arrive randomly. It may also be that there are other undiscovered craters either buried under sediments or on the ocean floor where they are less likely to be discovered.

Question 3.1

Mars has a semimajor axis around 1.52 AU. Using Equation 3.1 to calculate the length of the Martian year P_{Mars} in Earth days:

$$\frac{P_{Mars}^2}{P_{Earth}^2} = \frac{ka_{Mars}^3}{ka_{Earth}^3} = \frac{(1.52\ \text{AU})^3}{(1\ \text{AU})^3} = \frac{3.512}{1}$$

Therefore:

$$P_{Mars}^2 = 3.512\ P_{Earth}^2$$
$$P_{Mars} = \sqrt{3.512} \times P_{Earth}$$
$$= 1.87\ \text{Earth years.}$$

The Martian year is thus around 1.87 Earth years or 684 Earth days.

Question 3.2

From Equation 3.1:

$$\frac{P_{Pluto}^2}{P_{Earth}^2} = \frac{ka_{Pluto}^3}{ka_{Earth}^3} = \frac{(39.48\ \text{AU})^3}{(1\ \text{AU})^3} = \frac{61\,536}{1}$$
$$P_{Pluto}^2 = 61\,536\ P_{Earth}^2$$
$$P_{Pluto} = \sqrt{61\,536} \times P_{Earth}$$
$$= 248.1\ \text{Earth years.}$$

The orbital period of Pluto is thus 248.1 Earth years.

From Equation 3.3:

$$e = \frac{49.31 - 29.65}{49.31 + 29.65} = 0.249$$

The eccentricity of Pluto is thus 0.249.

Question 3.3

The correct assignments of the figures are:

a: Aten, Earth-crossing NEA with semimajor axis smaller than that of the Earth.

b: Amor, Earth-approaching NEA with orbit exterior to Earth's.

c: IEO, NEA with orbit entirely within that of the Earth.

d: Apollo, Earth-crossing NEA with semimajor axis larger than that of the Earth.

Question 3.4

Gravitational potential energy is at its greatest as the object reaches the position furthest from the Sun, known as the aphelion. This potential energy is converted to kinetic energy as an object moves along its orbit closer to the Sun because, in doing so, it accelerates. It gains the same amount of kinetic energy as it loses gravitational potential energy. After the object passes its closest approach to the Sun (perihelion), the kinetic energy is increasingly converted to potential energy until once again it reaches the aphelion.

Question 4.1

There are several examples of the dangers of misunderstanding the language scientists use to convey risk of an NEO impact which appear in Chapter 4. You might have chosen the phrase 'cannot rule out' used to describe the risk of asteroid 1997 XF11 impacting the Earth, a phrase which might be taken to mean there was a high probability of impact. The descriptions of low levels of risk which were used in the early version of the Torino Scale are another good example. In particular, for level 0 the phrase 'events having no likely consequences' in the earlier scale (Figure 4.3) was replaced by 'no hazard' in the more recent version. For level 1, the phrase 'events meriting careful monitoring' in the earlier version was replaced by the phrase 'normal' in the later version.

Question 4.2

(a) No, Tempel 1 is not an NEO because its current perihelion (around 1.5 AU) is more than 1.3 AU.

(b) At each gap in the table, the orbital parameters of Tempel 1 change, indicating that the orbit remains almost unaltered, for many years, but then undergoes a sudden change.

(c) You might have thought of as many as three likely reasons for a change in orbit:

(i) an impact with another body

(ii) a close encounter with a planetary body, resulting in significant gravitational perturbation

(iii) cometary activity (sublimation of ices from the surface) that jets the comet out of orbit.

Of the three possibilities, the third is unlikely because it would be expected to have a small effect every time the comet passes perihelion, rather than occasional, large changes. Impact with other objects is possible but unlikely to reoccur as often as seen in Table 4.2, and impacts big enough to cause such changes would probably destroy the comet completely rather than just change its orbit. The most likely answer is that Tempel 1 occasionally passes close to a large body and its orbit is perturbed. Indeed, Figure 3.7 shows that Tempel 1 passes close to the orbits of Mars and Jupiter. Because of its enormous size, Jupiter is most likely to cause orbital perturbations, as it did to comet Shoemaker–Levy 9.

Question 4.3

(a) The estimate based on lunar mare craters is 100–200 craters every 100 million years.

(b) The Earth and the Moon have accompanied each other throughout the last 4500 million years and they should have a very similar history of asteroid and comet impacts averaged over that period.

The numbers of craters are different but there may be several reasons for this difference. The Earth's greater gravity tends to increase the probability of attracting passing asteroids and thus there are likely to be more craters. However, this does not explain the curved line for terrestrial craters in Figure 2.17. The reason for the curved line for terrestrial craters is probably related to the tectonic activity at the Earth's surface, which buries and erodes craters, and the Earth's atmosphere which may cause larger asteroids to break up on entry, resulting in small craters or, in cases such as Tunguska, no crater at all. Both NEO break-up and crater loss by erosion and burial would tend to reduce the number of smaller craters. In addition, both cratering rates are estimates based on very different assumptions (e.g. 3600 million years versus 100 million years accumulation times). The uncertainty in each estimate is likely to be large and indeed the difference of a factor of 2.5 between the two estimates may be within the uncertainty.

(c) Figure 2.17 shows that 100–200 craters of between 20 km and 30 km diameter form approximately every 100 million years and telescope observations indicate about 167 kilometre-sized asteroids collide every 100 million years. Thus if 1 km asteroids cause craters between 20 and 30 km diameter, they should occur at a rate of about 167 every 100 million years. This crater formation rate coincides very closely with the rate derived from the lunar mare in the answer to part (b), and strengthens the hypothesis that the differences are likely to result from Earth's active surface, atmosphere, and greater gravity. The coincidence of figures also increases confidence that the numbers derived from very different data coincide and that scientists are increasingly able to estimate the risk of NEO impact on Earth.

Comments on activities

Activity 4.1

We placed the decision-making icon in five sections of Chapter 4. In Section 4.2, we asked you to consider the problem caused by differing conceptions of risk to decision makers.

In Section 4.3, we discussed issues related to the way in which science and scientists influence decision makers. Decision makers look to scientists as experts to both explain and inform them on scientific issues. However, the relationship between scientists and decision makers is not simple because government are also the funding body for much of academic research. Scientists' motivation in pursuing a particular line of research is overwhelmingly altruistic, but it has, in some cases, left them open to accusations of seeking to assist in covering up or 'crying wolf' to heighten awareness and acquire funding.

In Section 4.4, we saw that early asteroid scares and the impact of the comet SL-9 resulted in the US government reacting by increasing funding for NEO research and searches. A little while later, NASA established the NEO office in order to coordinate research and inform the public on the hazard. Following another close approach, questions were asked in the European Parliament. The UK government requested a report from the Parliamentary Office of Science and Technology, followed by a fuller report from a task force of experts. This resulted in greater international collaboration in searches for NEOs, research into the consequences and possible mitigation, and an office in the UK to relate clear information to the public.

Later, in Section 4.4, we saw decision making in action within the International Astronomical Union (IAU) on how, and when, to communicate risk to the public in regard to approaching NEOs. We saw the IAU consider how this was done in order to communicate clearly the real risk to the public.

In Section 4.5, we discussed the implications for decision makers of the discovery of an Earth-bound NEO, including disaster management and decisions concerning government actions, the timing of those actions and their consequences.

In Section 4.6, we saw what might be the most difficult aspect of decision making with regard to the NEO hazard: what would happen if one was going to hit or, indeed, the disaster management in the aftermath of an impact. In fact, should there be an impact in a populated area or in an ocean adjacent to a populated coastline, the decision makers are likely to be faced by a series of disasters that that have occurred before, including fire, flood and famine.

References and further reading

'Popular' books

Bell, J. and Mitton, J. (2002) *Asteroid Rendezvous: NEAR Shoemaker's adventures at Eros*, Cambridge University Press.

Cox, D. W. and Chestek, P. E. (1996) *Doomsday Asteroid: can we survive?*, Prometheus Books, New York.

Levy, D. H. (1995) *Impact Jupiter: the crash of Comet Shoemaker–Levy 9*, Perseus Books.

Lewis, J. S. (1997) *Rain of Iron and Ice: the very real threat of comet and asteroid bombardment*, Perseus Books.

Rubin, A. E. (2002) *Disturbing the Solar System: impacts, close encounters, and coming attractions*, Princeton University Press.

Spencer, J. R. and Mitton, J. (1995) *The Great Comet Crash*, Cambridge University Press.

Steel, D. (1997) *Rogue Asteroids and Doomsday Comets: the search for the million-megaton menace that threatens life on Earth*, Wiley.

Verschuur, G. L. (1998) *Impact!: the threat of comets and asteroids*, Oxford University Press.

Zanda, B. and Rotaru, M. (2001) *Meteorites: their impact on science and history*, Cambridge University Press.

Academic books

Belton, M. J. S., Morgan, T. H., Samarasinha, N. and Yeomans, D. K. (eds) (2004) *Mitigation of Hazardous Comets and Asteroids*, Cambridge University Press.

Bottke, W. F., Cellino, A., Paolicchi, P. and Binzel, R. P. (eds) (2003) *Asteroids III*, University of Arizona Press.

Hallam, A. and Wignall, P. B. (1997) *Mass Extinctions and their Aftermath*, Oxford University Press.

Lewis, J. S. (1999) *Comet and Asteroid Impact Hazards on a Populated Earth: computer modeling*, Academic Press.

Journal papers

Binzel, R. P. (2000) The Torino Impact Hazard Scale, *Planetary and Space Science*, **48**(4), pp. 297–303.

Chapman, C. R. and Morrison, D. (1994) Impacts on the Earth by Asteroids and Comets – assessing the hazard, *Nature*, **367**(6458), pp. 33–40.

Agency and governmental reports

Atkinson, H. et al. (2000) *Report of the Task Force on Potentially Hazardous near Earth Objects* [online], DTI/Pub4990/5k/9/00/NP.URN00/1041. Available from http://www.nearearthobjects.co.uk/report/pdf/full_report.pdf (accessed October 2005).*

Chapman, C. R. (2003) *How a Near-Earth Object Impact Might Affect Society* [online], commissioned by the Global Science Forum, OECD, for 'Workshop on Near Earth Objects: Risks, Policies, and Actions', January 2003, Frascati, Italy. Available from http://www4.tpg.com.au/users/horsts/chapman4oecd.pdf (accessed October 2005).*

Harris, A. W., Benz, W., Fitzsimmons, A., Green, S. F., Michel, P., Valsecchi, G. B. and Gálvez, A. (2004) *Space Mission Priorities for Near-Earth Object Risk Assessment and Reduction: Recommendations to ESA by the Near-Earth Object Mission Advisory Panel (NEOMAP)* [online]. Available from http://www.esa.int/gsp/NEO/doc/NEOMAP_report_June23_wCover.pdf (accessed August 2006).*

Morrison, D. (ed.) (1992) *The Spaceguard Survey: Report of the NASA International Near-Earth Object Detection Workshop*, (Jet Propulsion Laboratory and California Institute of Technology), prepared for NASA Office of Space Science and Technology.

NASA (2003) *Study to Determine the Feasibility of Extending the Search for Near-Earth Objects to Smaller Limiting Diameters: Report of the Near-Earth Object Science Definition Team* [online]. Available online at http://neo.jpl.nasa.gov/neo/neoreport030825.pdf (accessed October 2005).*

Remo, J. L. (ed.) (1997) *Near-Earth Objects: The United Nations International Conference*, New York Academy of Sciences.

UK Task Force Report (1999) Parliamentary Office of Science and Technology (POST), *Near Earth Objects – NEOs*, Report Number 126, April 1999.

* Electronic versions of these items can be found on the S250 DVD-ROM.

Acknowledgements

We would like to thank Neil McBride (Open University) for suggesting the NEOs topic.

Grateful acknowledgement is made to the following sources for permission to reproduce material within this book.

Cover photo David Parker/Science Photo Library.

Table 1.1 Chapman, C. and Morrison, D. (1994) Deaths per incident and probability of death by incident for various hazards, *Nature*, **367**, reprinted with permission from Nature.

Figures 1.1, 3.13 NASA/JPL images courtesy of Steve Ostro; *Figure 1.5* Courtesy of Dr D. Muller, University of Sydney; *Figure 1.6* NASA/ESA/STScI/ Science Photo Library; *Figure 2.1* Copyright © S. Eichmiller; *Figure 2.2* Photograph courtesy of Laboratory of Meteoritics, Vernadsky Institute, Moscow; *Figure 2.4* Tunguska Page of Bologna University http://www-th.bo.infn/ tunguska;
Figures 2.5, 2.10, 2.11, 2.15a–c Copyright © NASA/Science Photo Library; *Figures 2.6, 2.9a, 2.9b, 3.5, 3.13, 3.16, 4.2 and 4.6* Copyright © NASA; *Figure 2.7* Karen Carr; *Figure 2.12* Courtesy of Buck Sharpton and Lunar and Planetary Institute; *Figure 2.13* Copyright © Detlev Van Ravenswaay/Science Photo Library; *Figure 2.14a* Copyright © Kord Ernston; *Figure 2.14b* Courtesy of Robert Hough/OU; *Figure 2.14c* Iain Gilmour/Open University;
Figure 2.14d Copyright © Geoscience Features Picture Library; *Figure 3.3* Copyright © MPS 1986, 1996; *Figures 3.4a and 3.4b* 'Akira Fujii/David Malin Images'; *Figure 3.9* Harvard-Smithsonian Center for Astrophysics Observatory; *Figure 3.11 A philosopher lecturing on the orrery*, Joseph Wright of Derby, exhibited 1766. Derby Museums and Art Gallery; *Figures 3.14 and 3.15* Adapted from Stuart and Binzel, *Icarus*, 170, 2004; *Figure 3.17* © NASA/JHU-APL; *Figure 4.1* Sky Publishing Corporation; *Figure 4.3* Binzel, R.P. (2000) The Torino Impact Hazard Scale, *Planetary and Space Science*, **48**, Elsevier Science; *Figure 4.4* from Belton, M. (2004) *Mitigation of Hazardous Comets and Asteroids*, Cambridge University Press; *Figure 4.5* Alan B. Chamberlin, NASA/JPL.

Every effort has been made to contact copyright holders. If any have been inadvertently overlooked, the publishers will be pleased to make the necessary arrangements at the first opportunity.

Index

Entries in **bold** are key terms defined, along with other important terms, in the Glossary. Page numbers referring only to figures and tables are printed in *italics*.